Modeling of Thinking and the Mind

Preface

The advent of information theory and computer technology has focused the attention of science upon the functional aspects of mechanism in a new way. The hardware becomes of interest in terms of its information processing attributes. Systems are studied as interrelated configurations of information processing elements. The reductionist problem becomes one of finding the appropriate code rather than simply locating the site of action.

This orientation has been embraced by the scientific community within the Soviet Union in the name of their Cybernetic Program which attempts to generate "Scientific Government" (presuming, of course, the sanctity of some higher-level goal). This philosophic viewpoint has probably had greatest impact in the fields of biology and psychology where the concern is with the nature of thinking in terms of properties and mechanisms.

This book offers a survey of the state of the art as seen by an eminent scientist from his unique vantage point within the Soviet spectrum of activities. After examining fundamental considerations germane to the philosophy of science and the development of mathematical models, he proceeds to consider information processing at increasing levels of complexity within the living organism. Detailed considerations are devoted to intracellular homeostatic mechanisms, with the explicit recognition that homeostasis must be modifiable if there is to be learning. He proceeds to intercellular mechanisms, such as the endocrine system and the nervous system, finally focusing attention upon the information processing aspects at higher levels of human behavior.

Granted, some of the concepts presented in these latter chapters might be called speculative, they do, however, represent the direction of thought in this area of significant interest. Amosov apparently realizes the importance of this overall perspective in terms of computer realizations of artificially intelligent systems in the near future. He concludes, "It seems to me that it's simply unthinkable to plan the building of a new society without quantitative consideration of the psychology of its members." This demonstrates a new perspective in Soviet philosophy, a freedom of the scientist to offer precepts to those who control the Government. Their acceptance of this represents a new level of sophistication which might indeed result in dramatic changes in future Soviet policy with respect to science, internal politics, and even international development.

Throughout, there has been an attempt toward direct translation of Soviet terminology, except where recognized idioms are used. This book represents a worthy attempt to blend the common interests of biology, psychology, and engineering. It provides material of interest to the entire spectrum of those interested in science, technology and its impact upon the future of society.

LEO FINEGOLD, M. A.

LAWRENCE J. FOGEL, PH. D.

Modeling of Thinking and the Mind

N.M. Amosov

Translated by
Leo Finegold
San Diego Mesa College
for Scripta Technica, Inc.

Translation Editor
Lawrence J. Fogel
President, Decision Science, Inc.
San Diego, California

SPARTAN BOOKS
New York

Macmillan and Co., Ltd.
London

MODELING OF THINKING AND THE MIND

Printed in the United States of America.

Originally published under the title of MODELIROVANIYE
MYSHLENIYA I PSIKHIKI by Naukova Dumka Press, Kiev,
1965

Sole distributors in Great Britain, the British Commonwealth,
and the Continent of Europe:
        Macmillan and Company, Ltd.
        4 Little Essex Street
        London, W. C. 2

Contents

Introduction

Problems of thinking and of the human mind have attracted the interests of thinkers throughout history. Philosophers of antiquity, naturalists of the Middle Ages, the erudite of the Renaissance, and scholars thereafter have been concerned with just these problems. Today the mind is being studied by neurophysiologists, by psychologists, by psychiatrists, and by philosophers of various disciplines.

Marx, Engels, and Lenin explicitly define the materialistic essence of thought processes in a philosophic way: The brain is the substrate of thought and man's behavior is contingent upon it. However, even at the present time, some scholars adhering to idealistic concepts, do not agree with this thesis. They assert that nonmaterial forces of one form or another function in thinking, as for example, in telepathy. To declare such observations to be fiction would be unscientific. Insofar as there are doubts as to the methodological purity of such experiences, it is necessary to verify them employing the achievements of modern technology: It is possible that some factors will be confirmed and information transfer will be registered without the employment of the usual material agents. Of course, this would not in any way, by itself, invalidate the concept of materialism. It would simply be necessary to look for new physical forces which might be manifested only at the level of highly organized living creatures. We cannot rule out such a situation since it would be a mistake to view the processes of life merely as an interaction of such relatively large particles as atoms and molecules. If physics admits the existence of even smaller elements of matter than these elementary particles, it is certain that these too participate in living systems. It is possible that the organism might be that very indicator which allows one to discover the activity of such particles under some particular conditions.

I admit the possibility of "wireless" transmission of psychic events, but I suspect that their significance in human behavior is not great. However, this view is relevant only so long as the authenticity of telepathy still remains to be confirmed.

But this is what is important. It is trivial to acknowledge the brain as the material substrate of the psyche. One must demonstrate the mechanism of its activity. In what way does it direct the behavior of man? When this is done, many doubts will disappear as will the desire to make use of miracles as an explanation for some of our actions. This is a very difficult task. The brain consists of many billions of distinct nerve cells, and in turn, each of these cells consists of a huge number of molecules of different types. We no longer doubt that human actions are determined by molecular and cell interrelationships. But a final, all-embracing proof that this is so will require models which represent the structure of the brain and which will reproduce its function, that is the behavior of man.

Some philosophers assume that the total activity of a very complicated system cannot be reduced to a composite function of its more simple elements; I believe they are mistaken. Such a point of view would make it impossible in principle to develop an artificial model which would reproduce the basic functions of a complex system. To state this is tantamount to declaring: "The brain is material, thinking is its function, but it is impossible to understand its activity." The highest form of understanding of a system is the reproduction of its structure and function, if not in full, then at least in its main manifestations. Man is fully capable of such an achievement.

Until very recently it was impossible to even dream of working models of complex systems consisting of an astronomical number of elements. The "details" out of which man constructed his models were too large and "dead," being incapable of change. The situation today has changed, or at least is changing.

Technology is giving us new elements: first, electronic tubes, then semiconductors, now thin films and microminiature circuits. The construction of artificial working systems of great complexity, of high reliability, and of colossal speed has become a real possibility. In principle, it has become possible to create a model approaching the brain in complexity. The crux of the problem is how to arrange the elements in it so that by their interaction, the model would more or less completely duplicate the living organism. In other words, the problem is to create machines which have the programs equivalent to that of the brain.

Unfortunately, there are still many impediments in this direction. First, we have a poor understanding of the structure and function of the brain. Physiologists have given us only very gross models depicted by diagrams and in terms of words. One cannot expect more for the time being since their means of modeling — of comprehension — is quite limited. In reality it is exceedingly difficult to gain insight into the highly complex schematic of the brain, this apparatus consisting of billions of elements and of a much greater number of connections between them, all contained in a volume which hardly exceeds a cubic decimeter. One cannot expect to obtain schematics of the brain and a description of its programs in the immediate future.

Does this then mean that modeling of human thought and of the mind must be postponed for an indefinite time? Does this mean that we must acknowledge the participation of "higher forces" or that modeling is, in principle, impossible because of qualitative peculiarities of the mind which, therefore, apparently cannot be reduced to computation?

There is no justification for such pessimism. It does not pay to wait for the anatomists and physiologists to decode the brain. Science, has an alternative — to study human behavior as an integrated system and model it by means of technological elements without attempting to maintain anatomical or physiological similarity to the components of the brain. Nature has developed much that is interesting, but human genius competes quite successfully with her.

However, can we now begin to model man's mind as an integrated system? Do we have sufficient data? Unfortunately, the answer is no.

Two scientific disciplines study human behavior: psychology (which embraces the study of normal people) and psychiatry (that of abnormal people). Both of these sciences are at that stage of development where, for the time being at least, they cannot offer material for modeling. The fact of the matter is that a necessary condition for the creation of any model is computation, that is quantitative regularity. Up to the present time, these sciences have almost exclusively been governed by qualitative concepts. They describe their systems by words, by simple graphs, and only very rarely by numbers (and this only in very special cases).

Of course, psychologists and psychiatrists are not responsible for this. Human behavior is very complex and varied. It is determined by a multitude of the most diverse influences of external and internal origin. Until very recently, the variety of human behavior was discerned by sense organs only and was described in verbal terms. Instruments for sensing and recording were extremely limited.

Now the possibilities for an objective study of the human mind have substantially increased. Complex technological systems, universal or special purpose computers are capable of receiving and retaining extremely varied information over protracted periods of time. Methods for processing this information exist which permit rapid selection of the required data or for the discovery of new information. It is true that as yet there is no justification for exaggerating the potential capability of these machines relative to logical operations, but, with each passing year, this capability is growing. Machines can already actively retain more data relative to more or less narrow problems than can man. And what is more important, machines can manipulate this data far more quickly.

This permits one to express the essence of man in terms of a set of numbers at whatever level of detail is desired. Of course, we are still very far from that time when a numerical model will be complete, but its probability, that is, its degree of coincidence with the original, can already be significantly higher than that of the probability of those models which are stored in our memory and which are expressed by words.

Initially, of course, it is necessary to develop a method of investigation which rests upon appropriate technical mechanisms and codes which permit portrayal of the findings in terms of numbers. Programs are also necessary for the processing of such numerical data. All of this, taken together, can be called "contemporary instrumental" psychology or possibly "cybernetic" psychology.

To begin working towards the creation of this new direction in science, some hypotheses about the mechanism or program of human behavior is essential. Every investigation must have a goal which has been derived from one or more conjectures. Even with perfect technology, one cannot exhaustively study everything that is sensed. Man is too complex to expect rapid discovery of valuable data. Besides, psychology and physiology have already accumulated enough facts to offer quite a few assumptions which permit representation of the human mind in broad outline. Further investigations on a new level, resting on quantitative data, must substantiate some of these assumptions and refute others.

In general, an hypothesis about thinking and human behavior is essential. An hypothesis is a model which is expressed in words or schematics. It may be broad — embracing many aspects of behavior of the original system, or narrow — describing particular problems. It may be general or detailed. Thus, for example, the task of a physiological hypothesis, which interprets the meaning and reciprocal relationship of different anatomical and functional sections of the brain, is intended to characterize the behavior of man as an integrated system. I have already said, that the time has not yet arrived for such a broad and deep hypothesis, and I doubt that it will be possible to construct such an hypothesis utilizing conventional means. However, even now, many particular hypotheses about the influence of various anatomical formations of the brain on human behavior are sufficiently validated and are suitable for use.

One can compose an hypothesis in a purely "informational" way — a psychological construct which does not rest on the anatomy of the brain but which has as a base only experience according to which some structural scheme of internal relations is created which exhibits the required effect in a manner most similar to that of human behavior. I believe it justifiable to say that such a fictional man functions as a real one.

In this book an attempt is made to state a similar hypothesis. It has a most direct bearing on simulation insofar as:

1. every hypothesis is a model of a system which is expressed

in different codes and mechanisms. We have tried to make our model broader and more detailed;

2. our model is algorithmic, that is, from it one can create programs for computers or technical specifications for the development of special mechanisms which can reproduce various aspects of the hypothesis in an operating artificial system. In other words, these are algorithms for heuristic modeling. Of course, in order to acquire them it is necessary to be given sufficient data to quantitatively characterize the hypothetical interrelations.

Heuristic simulation is as valid a method for gaining knowledge as are experimental investigations. Experiments yield facts from which we draw conclusions about the system behavior; by these conclusions the hypothesis is verified. We can reverse this procedure: given some fact, and on this basis construct a hypothesis of behavior in order to derive new facts. If these coincide with the data of subsequent experiments, the hypothesis is verified.

The general task which confronts contemporary life science is that of increasing its precision: It is necessary to depart from qualitative descriptions and proceed to quantitative models. All this is relevant even to psychology. Its task is to create models of human behavior. Of course, these will be probabilistic and numerous. But techniques exist which are suitable for the selection and retention of appropriate ones. It is necessary to create methods of testing the mind which permit its quantitative evaluation so that there is the possibility of relating man to various models. Only after this will we be able to calculate the behavior of an individual and, what is still more important, of a group of different people under specified conditions. I am convinced that without such computation in the future, it will become impossible to plan important governmental policies.

1

Some General Assumptions
of Cybernetics

Cybernetics expresses general regularities in the activity of natural and artificial systems. I will try to present these in brief outline (I consider it necessary to make the reservation that some assumptions will not coincide with those which are generally accepted). We will begin with basic concepts.

System, program, information. A system represents some quantity of identical or different elements which have been interconnected into a unified whole. In this formulation everything is relative since one can consider systems with stable internal connections as elements. In chemical systems atoms are the elements, in biological systems atoms and molecules are the elements, in complex organisms, cells are the elements, this in addition to atoms and molecules. In human society, man is the element and also possibly things created by him. Moreover, the element may be very complex, its behavior is far from determined by the simple laws of physics and chemistry. However, this behavior can be characterized statistically within some probabilistic limits. It is not at all necessary to represent an element of a system as something strictly structured. It has some structural and energy characteristics and the complex dependencies between these may be different for different elements.

In very complex systems elements are combined into subsystems, into groups where the internal connections are stronger than external ones. Clearly, a quantitative description of a subsystem within the system is possible.

Connections are interactions of elements which cause these to be combined into systems. The concept of interaction is completely relative. Within this concept, it is easiest to comprehend some transfer of energy, however, interaction is realized also through material particles and substances (perhaps it would be more sensible not to delve deeply into this problem at the present time). Experience has suggested some ideas relative to the character of interconnections: there are internal and external connections, strong and weak connections. Internal connections unite elements within a system, external connections extend to other systems. One can determine the strength of connections in terms of the quantity of energy which is transmitted from one element to another in the process of their reciprocal activities, or as the relation of this energy to the total quantity. However, this is all entirely relative.   Thus, for example, one cannot express the strength of bonds between people through energy or matter in the general meaning of these words.

In addition, there are rigid and flexible connections. These ideas are most frequently associated with the spatial relations between material elements. With rigid connection spatial relations are preserved and with a flexible connection such a constancy is not obligatory.

Finally, the concept of direct and feedback connections is very important.   A direct connection is the influence of one element on another and the feedback connection is its reciprocal. It is true that there is an implication here of a temporal difference: at first we have a direct influence which then gives rise to a feedback influence.   Unfortunately, in practice we are far from having the capability of distinguishing them: the feedback influences may be stronger than the initial activities and the brief gaps in time frequently conceal the causal dependency between them.

Feedback connections are divided into positive and negative ones. With a positive connection the feedback influence is integrated with the initial activity and in this way increases the effect on "the output"; with the negative connection, on the other hand, the feedback influence is subtracted from the initial influence and thereby decreases the ultimate effect.

If an external stimulus acts on a system which activates positive feedback connections, the potential limit of the ultimate effect is rapidly attained. With negative connections, the effect on output grows slowly. However, much depends on the so-called coefficient of the feedback connection which determines that part of the effect on the output which is returned to the "input." The effect also depends upon the time (on the phase) of this return. Under specific conditions, a system can enter into an oscillating condition or even be destroyed.

In spite of the apparent conditionality of the concepts "element," "connection," "system," it is possible to express these quantitatively in different units, although the vocabulary of physics and chemistry is inadequate for this. It is necessary to enlist new concepts from the theory of information.

In the world everything changes. Elements (and, in fact, entire systems) change within and external to systems and influence one another, in other words, exchange energy or material particles. Their structure and potential energy changes, their capacity to influence other systems is altered.

Changes of a system are not disorderly. In the first place, they are limited by the systems structure, by the ties of the elements, by the character of the connection between the elements. Consequently, a system can sense various external influences and can itself demonstrate these. Some systems will sense one form of energy while other systems will sense another form.

It seems to me that a systems future potential change, defined by its structure, can conveniently be labeled a program. Every system whether large or small has a multitude of programs. Everything is a function of the complexity of the structure of the system and its receptivity to different external influences. Out of the many programs there is a realization of that program which is activated by a given external influence.

We can imagine an infinite variety of programs. The more complex the system, the greater the variety. A system composed of two elements has the least number of positional alternatives. In a system which consists of billions of elements, the diversity of their relations is essentially infinite. However, in reality, the possible diversity of changes of a system is much less than that which is theoretically possible. A system differs from a simple aggregation of elements in that its components are united by internal connections which interact within well-defined relationships. Therefore, the number of programs of even the most complex system is finite. The probability of realizing each program is a function of the probability of the corresponding external influences.

With fulfillment of a program there is a structural change of the system. The very first step in the execution of a program leads to a change of the system. This means then, that potential future programs of the system have also been altered. It is of course, true that cyclical changes of a system exist wherein there is periodic return to the original condition.

Every change of an element of a system in the process of execution of a program is subject to the laws of physics. The smaller the elements (such as the atoms in a living organism), the shorter the possible programs. Complex systems have complex programs which embrace large segments of time. The programs of a complex system are composed of the programs of its components, of its elements, of its subsystems. They all possess a probabilistic character: their execution is a function of external influence directly on the given element or through the mediation of other elements.

Elements, and in fact, any complex system, interact through fields, particles, substances. We may say that this is a physical aspect of the universe. However, in addition to this, there is another aspect — informational. The latter quite clearly manifests itself in the interaction of complex systems when they act on one another not only directly by the physical factor itself, but also by the change of the informational aspect in time or space taken separately from the physical agent and expressed in terms of other physical structures. We can say that in these cases information acts separately from physical influence. And so, information is a change of physical influence (or of a parameter of a system) in space and time, taken separately from its physical agent. Information is inherent in every object, substance, system, beginning with elementary particles and ending with cosmic systems insofar as they influence other systems.

However, only a complex system, capable of reflecting information in its own structure in the form of a model, can separate information from influence. Physical phenomena of mutual transformations of different forms of energy are the basis for the activity of such systems. Natural and artificial systems are capable of expressing some parameters through others. For example, the quantity of electrical energy passing through a conductor is defined in terms of the amount of heat generated. Insofar as light quanta alter the course of chemical reactions, these reactions serve as indicators of light flow. Similar transformations are realized in equivalent relations, but these may be far from exact and according to linear functions. In general, significant changes can be expressed through simple equivalents.

Information and its codes.   Information is formed by some complex system possessing its own structure and its own program. This means that a system can change in a specific manner as a function of its inherent internal mechanisms (programs), which are activated or are changed under the influence of external influences.

Modeling (informational) systems can be characterized by an altogether different complexity of structure and, consequently, even of their programs. However, in the most general form, there are common features inherent to programs of information formation. We can note the following stages in these:

1. The sensing of external influence. In a special block made up of molecules (or more complex particles) there is a transformation of received energy (quanta, field, mechanical energy of oscillations) into some other form of energy peculiar to this block.

2. The accumulation of structures which have been altered under external influence. The composite of these structures is a temporary model of the external influence for a determined segment of time. The process of accumulating such models may be termed temporary or short-term memory.

3. The comparison of a temporary model of sensed influence with invariant model-standards. For this purpose some group of structures which serve as standards are stored in the memory (in the permanent structure). The number of these may vary greatly as a function of the complexity of the modeling system (in the simplest case there being only one standard). In addition, there is the program which compares the temporary model of the

sensed influence with a standard model which may be realized in a multitude of variants. The concurrence of models upon comparison excites the next element of the system, which forms a "symbol" — that "portion" of the particular energy of the system which influences its external environment.

In this manner, as a result of the execution of its program, the informational system converts the influencing energy into its own, produces information and transfers it by a specific code — with portions of information represented by new physical phenomena or structures.

These very general features of information formation are inherent to any system from the simplest transducer which responds to variations of temperature by change of electrical current, to the most complex — man, who responds to the most varied external influences in an even more varied way. Particular programs (that is, periods of changes) which are limited by the structure and character of the external influence, are the basis of activity of all systems. This same general type of program is inherent to elements which initially produce information and to those which transform it at higher levels of a complex system. For example, a receptor converts light or heat energy into nervous impulses whose frequency is a reflection of the intensity of the external influence. On the other hand, from this flow of impulses new information is formed somewhere at higher levels of the nervous system, information which specifies whether or not it is light or dark, cold or hot.

The quantity of information generated depends on the complexity of the programs of the sensing informational system. Moreover, an entire series of properties unite systems which have the capacity to generate information:

1. Primary sensing and coding systems are generally sensitive to only one form of energy and select this type from any other which may be simultaneously emitted from an object.

2. Programs of systems are such that they establish different relations between the influence and portions of information produced. Both the type of energy and its limits, that is, "thresholds," are selected. Furthermore, there are various quantitative relationships between input and output within these limits, in other words, there are various degrees of nonlinearity. And the nonlinearity is itself variable: that is, other particular programs of the system may exert influence on it. The sensitivity of transducers to "age," temperature, and so forth, is common knowledge. To a still greater measure this relates to receptors whose sensitivity is determined by the condition of the organism. Such a process may be presented schematically as a change of the dimensions (or of the form) of a model of that standard with which a temporary model of a portion of the influence is compared. Besides this, the speed of formation of the new symbol, the encoding of information, is altered as, for example, the nervous impulse in a receptor.

3. Relations between the magnitude of the energy received at the input to the energy of the signals (of the symbols within the code) at the output are quite variable. A system can operate as an amplifier which converts insignificant external energies into quite powerful signals. The eye receptor and radio receiver operate in just this way. In other cases the reverse is true, that is, a signal of little power is produced at the output from a very powerful influence. For example, a man receives a powerful blow and falls; however, apart from this, his nervous system, through its own receptors, produces information in the form of many weak impulses. In the very same way, an ammeter generates information about the strength of the current in a cable transmitting thousands of amperes.

4. The difference in codes of the information being produced is a most important property. Signals at the output of the informational system (transmitter, receptor, cells at higher levels) correspond to different parameters (or changes of parameters) of signals at the input. And so, for example, a transmitter or receptor can send impulses proportional to: (a) the intensity of the influence, that is to the quantity (or the speed) of the energy received per unit time; (b) the total sum of received energy beginning from the moment of its arrival up to a determined limit of saturation; (c) the change of intensity (or the acceleration) of activity in time, or by a still higher derivative. Besides these, one can assume innumerable variants: the response to the sum or difference of two influences — by the principle of summation in space, the response to various combinations of the enumerated parameters. In all cases, the signal of the system or, in other words, the information generated by the system, is determined by the particular programs of that system.

The code is simultaneously the signal on the output of the modeling system and its meaning, that is, that portion of the external influence to which it corresponds in accordance with the program for generation of information.

If one imagines a graph of the function $x = f(y)$ according to which the external influence changes, then with different programs of the receiving system, many different codes of information can be produced. For example, several derivatives, the integral (the area) between specific values can change as a function of a shift of the coordinate axes, this corresponding to the addition of some constant magnitude. Finally, knowing the other function $y = x(z)$, one can obtain the cumulative relationship, and so forth.

In this manner, the quantity of information generated by the system from external influence is determined only by the sensing system and may only be compared to that of similar systems under the same condition. Thus, from external appearance and human speech, each of us generates his own information; the dog generates its own, the fly its very own. There is no complex apparatus which does not possess a corresponding program.

Information may be generated by any object regardless of whether or not it was deliberately stored.

Every information output is a physical process and, therefore, this very concept is somewhat relative and artificial. However, the utilization of informational concepts is convenient and very productive considering the contemporary level of science. In- formation replaces true physical phenomena by their equivalents expressed as physical symbols but these are far more simple and more suitable for manipulation. Animals and until recently, people, utilized information without even suspecting its existence. In particular, all of mathematics and indeed, science in general, is pure information. We have now "understood" this and have begun to consciously utilize it, primarily, for modeling with the aid of new technical means. The model and memory are the bases for the generation of information.

The model is a structure (a physical model, which exists independently or which is composed of elements of a more complex simulating apparatus), in which a change of external influence in space or time (information) is expressed. The degree of similarity between the model and the object is determined by the programs of formation of the given model in the process of generating information about the object. A model is made up of some structural elements, from a specific sequence of "small models": of symbols within the code, of standards.

Models are stored in memory. Memory is a complex concept which has several meanings. From one aspect, it is the "depository" of models: the structure in which the models are imprinted, or simply a collection of them as physical systems. Another aspect is that memory is a property of complex systems which stores (preserves) information about activities. Short-term memory is an accumulation of models of the immediately received information expressed in structures of the "input code." They can disappear at once following comparison with constants (as in a transmitter) or may remain for some time (as models of images in the brain). Permanent memory preserves models of code symbols, standards, models of programs (see below). Finally, a system can possess "output memory," in which information is reflected not in the form of models of the input code, but in the form of the sequence of models of particular code symbols.

In natural simulating systems (to a lesser degree in mechanical systems), models remain unaltered in the memory. Elements, which comprise these, "live" according to their programs and can change with time. In this way, models change.

Reprocessing of information. As already indicated, production of information is a physical process. The code symbols of information are physical magnitudes (for example, nerve impulses, sounds, portions of chemical substances). If information, which has been expressed by physical symbol-signals, is transmitted by some connection, then it may be considered as an independent physical activity, into which, information has not premeditatively been placed by anyone. Thus, fluctuations of the air which are produced by the human voice are not in any way distinguishable by the fly from those of a breeze, though, in the former, information has been introduced in contrast to the latter in which no information has been imparted.

Hence, the stream of primary information may be subjected to the very same processing as any physical influence. In other words, new information may be derived from this stream.

Secondary information is generated by the very same principles as those applicable to the production of primary information:

1. Influence (information, expressed by physical magnitudes) is sensed and a temporary model, divided up into separate portions, is created from it.

2. From a specific program, a comparison of models of these portions is made with standard models of symbols of a new code; such standards being retained in the permanent memory.

3. At each point in time a symbol is given off at the output; consequently, the primary flow of information moves into a new channel by means of an already-formed new higher-level code.

4. Secondary information can be reflected in the memory in the form of a model composed of a sequence of new symbols of the code.

It is possible to produce a multitude of secondary codes from primary information, as, for example, from primary physical influence we derive an instantaneous magnitude, a sum for an interval of time (integral), derivatives, sums and differences with other functions, and so forth. Everything is a function of the program of the informational system and of the symbols of the corresponding codes (Fig. 1).

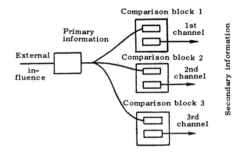

FIG. 1. Generation of secondary information. In comparison blocks 1, 2, 3, a temporary model of primary information is compared with models-standards of different codes-qualities. Secondary information is given off as three different codes.

As an example, let us examine the way in which information generated from speech sounds is reprocessed.

The ear senses oscillations and codes them by means of nerve impulses which are directed to the cerebral cortex. At the first level, a temporary "model of sounds" is formed — the models (images) of separate sounds which have been combined in time. It is broken into portions corresponding to words. The latter are compared with permanent models of words which correspond to one's own specific code, that is, there is a complex of cells corresponding to each word. As a result of the comparison, information is encoded by means of a new code, by a code of words, it is transmitted to the next level of the cortex. A new temporary model of the information is formulated there and transcribed by the more economical code of words. Once again a comparison is made with models of a code; this time, a code of phrases, and information is transmitted to the next level. Here the very same thing occurs: generation and modeling of a higher level code, that of meaning. At each level, information becomes more general, more abstract, but occupies less space in the memory.

In speech, only one code is employed, that of sounds and the letters corresponding to them. The generation of information at higher levels occurs in the cerebral cortex of every person. However, it is possible, in principle, to compose a code of words and even a code of sentences. Of course, it would be difficult to retain the obtained multitude of symbols as a result of this; but the information would be recorded very economically. In fact, this very thing is done in computers which utilize corresponding "alphabets" of words, and concepts.

The probabilistic principle of recoding is very important. Portions of information, recorded in a lower level code, only approximately correspond to the symbols of a higher level code. One advanced symbol may correspond to several variants of lower models. For example, many variants of sentences may possess one meaning approximately, many variants of sound pronunciation may correspond to one word. Upon recoding of information by a higher level code, a part of the information will be unavoidably lost: the recorded words lose expressiveness, peculiar to the way in which they have been pronounced. If it were possible to record speech in terms of a "meaning code," then different nuances of phrases would disappear. Thus, the related contents of a book are always poorer than the book itself.

Different degrees of "inflexibility" of recoding exist, that is, degrees of probability (of approximation) of the correspondence of the model transcribed by a lower level code to the symbol of the higher level code. Thus, words rigidly correspond to letters (less rigidly to sounds), and the correspondence of the meaning of sentences to their inscription is quite approximate.

One can formulate some propositions which specify the recoding of information by means of higher level codes (by alphabet):

1. A code characterizes the quality of information and the quality of the system. Therefore, we can speak of code-quality.

2. A higher-level code is obtained upon the integration of information which has been transmitted from a lower-level code.

3. The higher the code, the greater its symbolic content (or of their models).

4. Every higher-level code has greater capacity, thus, is more economical. Upon moving to a higher-level code, large portions of information are replaced by individual code symbols.

5. The generation of symbols of a higher-level code from information which has been transmitted by means of lower-level codes is accomplished by a probabilistic comparison and not an exact comparison with models in the form of reference symbols (standards).

6. Many higher-level models can be selected from the same information transmitted by lower codes, provided different systems of symbols of higher-level codes are utilized.

7. Upon recoding information in terms of a higher-level code, a part of that information is unavoidably lost. Losses may in part be compensated if several systems of higher-level codes are utilized.

8. Higher-level codes are more abstract than lower-level codes.

9. Complete information about a system is retained only when the models which occur are comprised of symbols of a lower-level code.

10. Higher-level codes may be produced from information (a model) represented by a lower-level code provided the method of recoding is known. The reverse procedure is impossible without a significant loss of information.

11. The more complex the system, the greater the number of levels of codes and models of information the system can produce from the sensed influences.

Hierarchical processing of information is advantageous because it demands less memory capacity and selection of the required information is facilitated — a crude selection is accomplished in processing according to models of the higher-level code, precision being subsequently accomplished with lower-level models (something analogous to this occurs in the compilation of a bibliography).

Information is produced within a receiving system only when systems physically interact. Although memory can be vested in physical activity, its discovery rests upon a capacity for modeling.

The process of generating models at several levels also produces distortion of the information actually contained in the influence or directly vested in the activity of the transmitting system. The sources of distortion are as follows:

1. The sensing of a complex influence is limited by the possibilities of the sensing mechanism, that is, by the quantity and characteristics of the receptor-transducers.   For example, a person senses only specific frequencies of sound waves and some portion of the light spectrum. He does not sense electromagnetic waves at all. Furthermore, insofar as the receptor characteristics are nonlinear, changes of physical influence are reflected in a manner disproportionate to their magnitude.

2. The volume of received information is determined by the possible number of models or symbols of the code. Those portions of the influence for which comparison has not found a reference are lost. Everyone knows this: hearing a complex report, we perceive only that portion of it which is accessible to our understanding — that portion for which there are corresponding symbols of the meaning code.

3. The probabilistic comparison of portions of information with models or symbols in the code is also a source of distortion since several symbols of a higher-level code can approximately correspond to a single portion recorded by a lower-level code even with different degrees of probability. The selection of one of these is determined by the program of the simulating mechanism.

It is interesting to inquire as to the quantity, quality, and value of information. Recently, great interest has been exhibited in calculations of the quantity of information in terms of bits. I think that there is little validity in this approach since information cannot be directly equated to matter or energy, since information also possesses quality. Measuring information in terms of a single metric is tantamount to comparing the value of a kilogram of the brain to a kilogram of stone, formally considering only that each has identical mass.

It seems to me that the quality of information is determined by the code by means of which the information is generated from the simulating system.   For example: in examining an object, we can identify its form, coloration, its illumination. These are all qualities of the object which are produced by simulation of the light reflected from the object into the eyes in the cerebral cortex. In the cortex, the light flow is reprocessed with the help of different codes-qualities: for the production and recognition of form, another is for color, and so on. The system of codes is extremely varied; it is, therefore, possible to produce an infinite number of qualities. An exact demarcation between properties and qualities cannot be made. I think that properties are depicted by information having "parallel" codes—in terms of form, of color, etc. Both systems of the code lie at the same level for the generation of information just as it is possible to produce a derivative magnitude and the integral from a single physical influence. A system of qualitative codes reflects a new level of information. To illustrate, evaluation of an objects capacity for displacement or change of form will be produced at one level. Information concerning the objects capabilities appear at a still higher level, for example, its capacity to be trained. In order to generate such information as external symbols of the objects behavior, its movements as a function of surrounding conditions must be reprocessed at a higher level of the cerebral cortex.

Of course, no sharp boundary exists between codes of properties and codes of qualities. The quantity of information can be formally expressed in terms of the number of symbols of the code which have been transmitted during some time interval; however, such a definition is of little value. Thus, in a code of letters, every letter is a unit. If a code for the meaning of phrases existed, let us say, expressed by written symbols — then, of course, the number of such signals and the quantity of stored information would greatly exceed the corresponding number of letters. Words themselves, as units of meaning codes, contain widely different quantities of information (for example, the information contained in the word "revolution," is incomparably greater than that in the word "stone").

One can calculate the quantity of information contained in a signal within some artificial limitations through use of mathematical information theory. If the measure of information is understood to be a measure of increase of specificity, then, in order to calculate the information one can artificially select two neighboring levels. Thus, in the process of compiling a word which designates a specific concept, that is, a particular symbol of a higher-level code, every succeeding letter bears a different quantity of information, expressed in units of a lower code, that is, in terms of the letter code.

In general, it seems to me that quantitative calculations of information are not well-justified except for narrow areas of utility.

The concept of value of information is still another thing. Common place examples illustrate the different value of the same communication for different people. This is natural: information is separately generated by each informational system and can be compared only with a comparison of these systems. The value of information for a given system is determined by those changes which will occur in the system after reception of signals, in other words, by means of programs activated by these signals. In order to specify the information quantitatively, one must express the state before and after the reception of signals in some units, or, more correctly, the relationship of the previous to the subsequent programs. For example, programs of activity are stored in a healthy man which can be conditionally expressed in units of work completed up to the onset of natural old-age. Suddenly he receives word of the death of a very close friend. The result is a serious mental illness, an alteration of all of the programs, a

sharp limitation of his capacity to work and, consequently, a decrease
in the quantity of his actual work. The difference in programs before
and after reception of the information is an expression of that in-
formations value. Of course, this is all quite academic since it
is not easy to evaluate programs which are themselves expressed
in concepts of information having a hierarchical construction.

And so, the hierarchical structure of information, of its codes
and models, encumbers or even makes it impossible to measure
the quantity of information by any single measure covering both
lower and higher levels. Measurement is possible only within the
limits of a single level (of one code-quality) or upon the comparison
of identical systems.

Programs, their essence and development. A general definition
of programs has already been given — the possibility for the change
of a system which has been stored within its structure. In other
words, a program may be defined as a sequence of activities executed by the system in relation to all of the systems which surround
it.

This concept seems basic because a program defines itself by:
1. its physical influence on other systems;
2. its informational influences on these same systems; and
3. the generation of information from the received influences.

Thus, all "behavior" of a system, that part which participates
in the analysis of the surrounding world and that part which influences the surrounding world, is determined by the program.

Naturally, this concept is in accordance with the general principle of causality. It is true that this principle is subject to criti-
cism where elementary particles are concerned, but when it is
applied to larger systems which conform to statistical laws, it is
certainly valid.

The development of systems has proceeded with an ever increasing complexity of their structure, and, consequently, there has
been an increasing diversity of programs. Material particles,
randomly colliding, combine under favorable conditions and these
combinations are more or less stable relative to subsequent external activities in regard to other systems. Different particles,
having different possibilities of combination, provide the basis of
matter, and to this extent are the prospects for the formation of
systems of any degree of diversity, unlimited in relation to both
the number and methods of combination of the particles. With
increasing complexity of systems, every particle (or, at least, the
majority of them) still retains some capacity for combination with
others; if follows that there is an unlimited increase in the number
of possible changes of a system — of its programs. A simple
analysis of the evolution of nature and of man's progress readily
corroborates this.

The general order of development of systems up to recent times
(from a geological point of view) proceeded as follows: random

changes of structure which lead to changes of programs and reinforcement of those changes in the process of "natural selection."
Those systems proved adaptive which were simultaneously stable
in form and sufficiently flexible so as "not to lag" in the struggle
for existence with respect to other systems which changed according to these same principles.

However, at some point in the history of human civilization,
the principle of random changes was violated with the progressive
substitution of directed change of the world by way of creation of
new systems having planned properties.

In general, the evolution of systems with regard to their complexity consists of a series of stages.

Originally, molecules of simple organic combinations developed.
Then, some of these molecules acquired the capability of combining
with one another thus forming long chains capable of reproduction
by separation "across" or doubling along the longitudinal axis.
The DNA and RNA molecules are the contemporary prototypes of
such chains. These are long chains of amino acids and sugars and
have the capacity to reprocess information with elevation of the
level of the code. As a matter of fact, these chains join with comparatively simple radicals to yield more complex systems capable
of performing the very same activities. Evidently, a primary
distinction of living systems is the reprocessing of information
with elevation of the level of the code. It is true that the informational aspect of the activity of the simplest linear systems is still
quite insignificant.

The next stage, evidently, was the generation of planar systems:
several long linear chains did not move apart following separation
but, instead remained connected, forming a system which possessed
some general programs — for movement, for the exchange of substances, and for reproduction. "Transverse" connections between
the chains created additional possibilities with respect to the complexity of the programs and this imparted greater stability to the
systems.

A new step in evolution was the appearance of a "superstructure" — a second level, heralding the generation of spatial systems
(Fig. 2).

In linear and planar systems, all primary chains (subsystems)
performed "worker" functions in the exchange of small particles
with the external environment, then in the new systems there
appear complexes of molecules which solely perform regulatory
functions. These molecules receive information as to the state of
the lower level as a function of external influences, reprocess this
information and, operating "from top to bottom," change programs
of the lower working level in a favorable way which ensures maximum adaptability to the changing external environment.

Very likely, the cell which has been built up from complex
molecules is the simplest example of such a hierarchical system.

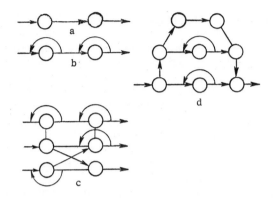

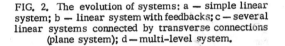

FIG. 2. The evolution of systems: a — simple linear system; b — linear system with feedbacks; c — several linear systems connected by transverse connections (plane system); d — multi-level system.

The lower level of the cell consists of chains of working reactions, which ensure the seizure and the reprocessing of food, movement, and so forth. These chains respond directly to external stimuli. The second level is regulatory. In this level, information is accumulated concerning slow and prolonged changes of the external environment and programs for the regulation of operations of the lower level are stored as a function of these changes. And finally, a third level, evidently determines the program of reconstruction, associated with the processes of reproduction. Contemporary cytology has already revealed chemical structures which correspond in their functions to these levels — various DNAs and RNAs.

A one-celled entity represents quite a complex system with great possibilities for hierarchical information processing. Nevertheless, the diversity of the one-celled structure is limited by the dimensions of the cell.

One-celled organisms comprised the first level of systems in the development of the organic world. Further complexity of living substances was expressed in the appearance of systems at a second level in which the molecular structures were supplemented by structures of cells. Various cells which possessed "specialized" programs (having greater capacity for contraction, digestion, or reception of external influences) in addition to identical general cellular programs, were combined into a single system, which possessed a significantly greater diversity and consequently still more complicated programs. Later, cell structures became divided into levels—worker and regulatory organs being isolated, thereby yielding a significant increase in the number of programs.

Nature has created a great number of different multicellular organisms — leading all the way up to man.

Communities of living organisms were the next level in complexity of systems. However, only for some types (as for example, insects) did these communities develop into relatively stable systems. Most likely, ant and bee colonies can be considered to be only relatively complex since they in no way exceed the diversity of colonies of some of the higher mammals.

Human communities are another matter. They have really been transformed into a very complex, completely stable system at a third level. In human society three levels of diversity can be sharply distinguished: structures comprised of molecules represent cells; structures comprised of cells represent individuals; and structures comprised of people represent society. To this it is necessary to add other things — models, created by man which occupy a firm place in the general system of "humanity." Thus, a very complex system of colossal diversity has been generated and, consequently, the programs are most diverse as well.

We can note some regularities in the process of development of systems:

1. The separation of structures into those substructures which obtain and process information as distinct from those which simulate and perform the operations themselves, that is, those structures which impart information to the outside. Of course, this division cannot be imagined to be a complete separation, since all information processing, both input and output, is realized by programs which have much in common. There are always elements which influence the external world as they examine it, other elements which are intended to influence or change the external world, and still other elements which are intended to introduce corrections into the program (feedback). Moreover, such a division can be expressed in various ways in systems of different levels. For example, we can point to the distinction of the "feeling" and motor sections of the nervous system in terms of nerves leading to the cerebral cortex.

2. Systems of increasing complexity were not spontaneously generated but rather compiled from already existing simpler systems which had their own programs. As a result, conflict may exist within complex systems. On the one hand, following such a combination, overall programs of the new system appear and, on the other hand, the programs of the constituent systems are still preserved, and these may frequently be at variance with the "main" program. In the process of evolution, ancient programs are not destroyed, but are only limited and suppressed.

The matter is quite different with respect to artificial systems created by man: although in these systems there are particular and general programs, their contradictions are significantly less sharp.

Questions of interaction of programs in complex systems require a more detailed examination. First of all, let us examine the relations between working and "informational" controlling levels.

We can represent these as two cycles of complex chemical reactions which have their own direct and feedback connections which provide self-regulation. Both cycles are connected with each other "by vertical" influences, as, for example, in the form of some final or intermediate chemical substances. Influences from "bottom to top" reflect selection of information; from "top to bottom," the control of operations, that is, of working programs. With this, one can imagine different degrees of dependency of both chemical cycles — from zero to one. In the first case with disruption of the connections the reactions can proceed almost without alteration, in the second case — the reactions are immediately stopped. This is the energetic dependence or the physical aspect of the connection. Another aspect is informational. The second level selects information from the programs of the first level. This process is possible with little energy exchange. The information can be more or less complete — as a function of the program of reprocessing and as a function of the forms of the sensed influences. In the simplest case, the upper informational level senses only "yes" or "no" in relation to certain possible changes on the lower level. On the other hand, it bears a controlling function in relation to the lower working level. The latter may also have a different capacity — from simple activation or deactivation to detailed control of many processes with different rates of change.

Consequently, different energetic (physical) and informational dependencies may occur in the relations between the first and second levels. The code of information selected "above" determines the influences which direct various aspects of the activity of the working elements at the lower level.

Relations between "neighboring" structures-programs can be similar. Each structure-program has its own working functions and in addition senses information about its "neighbor" and influences this neighbor in energetic and informational (regulatory) ways.

The range of cross influence of neighboring and hierarchical structures within a system and their programs is infinitely rich, but one can identify some typical trends:

1. Subordination is the coordination of programs at lower levels to higher ones. At a higher level, a model of the program of regulation of the lower levels is stored. This model does not replace the activity of the lower level in detail, but directs it, acting on some links of the chemical chains of transformation.

2. Synergism is the parallel activity of neighboring structural formation (subsystems) in which programs supplement one another. Applied to living systems, this means an exchange of intermediate products resulting in gain for both systems, a mutual stabilization of activities: insufficiency of one program is compensated for by the other.

3. Antagonism (struggle, contradictions). In this case, one subsystem inhibits the activity of the other. In terms of the chemistry

of living substances, antagonism manifests itself with the secretion of special substances which restrain some chemical reactions (inhibitors), in other systems, by the activity of special information on different levels.   Struggle may be expressed in terms of physical relations: It can be manifested in relation to physical forces which operate antithetically, or in terms of informational influences — signals which block certain programs and excite others.

4. Noises.   There are cases when the execution of a program is encumbered because of extraneous influences which in themselves do not represent an antagonistic signal but which distort useful information.   In technology, such phenomena are designated as noises.   Evidently, this concept is applicable to all hierarchical programs.   Several types of noise can be distinguished depending on their level or origin.   With noise from "below," the execution of a program at some higher level is encumbered by the particular programs of the lower structural units which do not correspond to higher control influences.   For example: all cells of the human organism must, by their own activity, ensure the execution of the total (main) programs activated by the cortex.   However, muscle cells and cells of internal organs have their own programs which impose limitations on the main programs: the liver yields little glucose, the heart muscle provides insufficient blood, and the brain therefore experiences an oxygen debt and is compelled to alter its own program.

In addition to such direct "program" noncorrespondence of levels, physical noise exists which comes "from below."   The point is, that signals in the form of other physical influences of a completely different lower level may impinge on signals which transmit information and are expressed as physical phenomena. This is apparent in electronic apparatus having so-called noise. Distortion of signals of one subsystem arise even in the case where useful signals of a similar neighboring system are physically imposed on them, as for example, in the simultaneous conversation of several people.

From the "point of view" of a given subsystem which has its own programs, the control signals may be considered as noise which enter from a higher level, for example, muscle cells "want" to rest after work since decay products have accumulated within them.   But man must work and he compels his muscles to contract to complete exhaustion.   Clearly, this is detrimental to cellular programs.

Of course, these ideas concerning the interrelationships of programs are highly conditional.   One cannot sharply distinguish them. In particular, one cannot separate antagonism from noise on a single level or noise from "above" from control signals.   One thing is clear: everything that obstructs the execution of a given program of a specific structure can be interpreted as noise.

In complex multileveled natural systems, there are always all components of relations between programs. The principal quality of the system, its stability against external destructive influences, is determined by their correspondence.

Interrelationships of programs within a system are still further complicated by the fact that the very same elements (or subsystems) can take part in the execution of different programs, that is, enter into different models. This is explained by the diversity of connections between elements (if they are complex) or between subsystems. Therefore the "degree of independence," or the stability of different models-programs within a system is quite varied. There are "stable" models and correspondingly well-developed programs, but there are also many other models which are realized only under specific favorable conditions when the elements which enter into them are not "occupied" in other programs.

Every well-defined complex system has its own main programs which characterize it as a single unit and distinguish it from other systems — from higher and lower ones. For example, the main programs of a one-celled organism are movement, growth, and reproduction; of contemporary man, the capacity for work, for making things. Of course, in addition to the main programs, complex systems have many secondary programs. Insofar as the program is a physical operation, that is, concerns the selection of external information, it is necessary to use a special code for its realization. By this code, the microbe will produce new variants which exercise a changing or destructive influence on other living creatures. The basic code of complex animals is physical movement which influences the surrounding world. The code of man's movements, as a product of society, is even more perfected, having been transformed into the code of speech, a code of things. This is the highest code and possesses a great diversity of symbols.

The code determines the quality of a system — its code-quality. Systems of different complexity and specificity will be separated by a code of externally transmitted information: here lies their qualitative distinction. There is a direct relationship between the number of programs of a system and the number of its qualities. However, not all programs characterize the "novelty" of a system since the majority of programs are not distinct from programs of other, lower systems. The major part of the programs of activity of man's internal organs is similar to programs of other advanced mammals and only programs of behavior which have been inculcated by society have made man the creature that he is.

The main programs of a complex system do not constitute something new or spontaneously generated. They are the results of summation, or more precisely of integration of many simpler programs of the lower levels of the structure. One can, therefore, characterize them through the physics of these structural units.

For example, speech is a very complex program, but it is described by particular programs of nerve cells which direct the muscles of the larynx and of respiration. Knowledge of lower programs of subsystems permits the development of a higher program of the entire system. However, this in no way means that a simple collection of lower programs is the equivalent of a higher program. To obtain the latter, a model in the form of the structure must be created. Thus, the ability to pronounce sounds still does not constitute speech. For speech to occur there must be a higher-level model in the cerebral cortex in which the sequency of activation of particular models for the pronunciation of the separate sounds is imprinted. A multitude of levels of thought are arranged over these models, levels in which models of various combinations of words and simple phrases are stored. In other words, a specific structure (a model) must enter into the composition of a complex system, one which is the bearer of a higher-level program which determines the quality of the system. In man these are models of thought, of movements embracing large intervals of operating time. In animals, there are similar models but these are less varied and involve shorter segments of time. In society, as in a system, physical models are the vehicles for higher programs — for things, books, apparatus, in which history, science, and art are imprinted. Simultaneously, these programs are expressed through people who represent the "controlling structure" of society, its political representative, scientists, in exactly the same manner as cells of the cortex and cortical models from these cells represent structural units which control the behavior of man.

The basic program of the system can be constructed from the particular programs of all the components of a complex system. However, the reverse cannot occur — the particular subprograms cannot be reproduced from a main program. More properly, it is possible to invent new systems and new programs, which in summation will yield a specified higher-level system, but this would be a different system with different lower-level programs. Thus we can record speech but we cannot exactly reproduce the programs of the nerve cells and muscles of the throat which together provide for the pronunciation of the words of the speech. We can only devise new artificial organs which simulate our speech, but these organs operate according to programs completely different from those of the living system.

The possible diversity of complex systems is immense. Any higher-level program can be obtained by way of many combinations of different lower-level programs. The question reduces to this: which combination of lower-level programs will yield a better variant. All higher-level programs are built in an informational way and therefore different physical elements can be employed for their creation. The process of thinking and the other complex operations of man are higher-level programs built from specific combinations of a multitude of elements — of nerve and muscle cells which have their own cell programs. But what is most important is not that cells are complex biological systems, but that the combination of these cells and the derivative structures provide the model for information processing. Therefore the creation of an artificial thinking system is fully possible, a system which is constructed from other elements, but which in total reproduces that very advanced high-level program — thought. This new system would probably occupy a huge volume and would not be able to execute other programs which are inherent to man. The possibility of creation of an "artificial man" is theoretically possible, a "man" who possesses all the entire programs of the prototype, but this would have to be built of technological and biological elements.

Complex systems with great capacity for self-organization, in other words, those which do not possess a rigidly fixed structure, can execute the same general programs by different "particular" means. In man, insofar as his structure is rigid, the principle of self-organization is not expressed and only in the cerebral cortex are new functional structures formed owing to the selection of many redundant connections. Nevertheless, even man can express his thought by different means — by speech, writing, and through mimicry. He can write with both his right and with his left hand, even with his feet. In such an active structure as society, advanced programs (for example, change of a specific direction) can be realized in completely different particular ways. The whole problem resolves itself into how quickly and economically these can be realized.

The concept of "complexity" of a system is quite relative. Complexity is not merely the quantity and diversity of elements and subsystems constituting a system, but the diversity and complexity of programs of behavior as well. Are there criteria for the determination of the complexity of a system? Evidently, complexity can be measured only upon comparison of the system with other systems or through a process of competition between them. However, only similar homogeneous systems may be compared. What does a mountain and man have in common? A mountain can crush man, but even a man, as a part of society, endowed with his technological achievements, can destroy a mountain. Perhaps, the primary criterion for the complexity of regular systems is their survival capability in conflict and their disposition or stability in the face of external influences. In any event, with extreme diversity of systems and of their programs, comparison is possible only through their modeling within specific degrees of simplification, when any one quality is isolated, and within these limits a quantitative determination is made. The general "level of complexity" of a system can be evaluated in terms of the time interval of its programs, models of which are stored in control organs. An animal plans its activities in advance by minutes or hours, a child by days, an adult sometimes by his whole life or minimally, in terms of years.

However, all these criteria are quite relative.

The principal total programs of a complex system which determine its qualities are provided by an entire series of particular programs for information processing. I will limit myself to an enumeration of some of these main programs (they will be considered in detail using human behavior as an example):

1. The basic quality of complex programs is their flexibility. This means several variants of programs on a lower level correspond to a general model of a program at a higher level; from these variants, that one is selected which is most suitable at a given moment as a function of different local conditions sensed by feedback and communicated from "above." For example: A person has an idea, at a higher level of the cerebral cortex for the performance of a motor act which strives for a specific goal. The execution of the idea, that is, the selection of extremities and muscles which will accomplish this act, is determined by the conditions obtaining at the moment of initiation of the movement (one arm is occupied, a finger hurts, and so forth). The selection proceeds automatically on the periphery.

2. A program of "foresight" is an activity which is "worked through" on models before actually beginning. The selection of an optimum variant is then made, not at the periphery, but "in the center."

3. A program of "goal" is the mobilization of supplementary means for completion, regardless of noises from different levels, of some one program, selected for one reason or another.

4. An antithetical program is the selection of a more effective activity as a function of external stimuli for the given moment. Orienting to change in the situation, a switchover is made from one program to another.

The best program is a combination of conditions mentioned in the last two points: the main program is preserved and the changing circumstances only vary "subprograms" for its execution.

5. Execution of the main program under difficult conditions when the existence of a system is threatened provides the "programs of emergency amplification" which activate the supply of reserves and which regulate the expenditure of these reserves for brief time intervals.

6. The most important program of the most complex systems is "creativity," that is, the creation of new models from elements of old models. Creativity is accomplished initially in the interior of the modeling system and then in the form of physical models — of things.

7. The program of self-learning is a consideration of the experience of execution of former programs for the selection of an optimal variant under new, but similar conditions.

8. Unfortunately, due to the limitation of the memory capacity of the system, forgetting, as contrasted to the learning capacity — that is the extinction of old models which have "not been employed" for a long period of time or which do not have meaning for the execution of the main program at the given time.

In all probability, this does not exhaust the list of important programs which are characteristic of complex systems.

Cognition as modeling. Every cognition is a modeling of information about another system through programs of a modeling mechanism which cognizes the system. This process is possible only in the presence of connections (interactions) between the object and subject of cognition. The results are models which are determined by these connections and by others although not to an equal degree.

A model is a structure which exists separately or within a complex modeling mechanism; a structure which to some degree reproduces the structure and program of an object, but which never makes an identical copy of that object. Simultaneously, programs of the subject — of the modeling mechanism — are reflected in the model.

The process of cognition-modeling is a program for the selection of information. As we have already pointed out, this program consists of the following stages:

1. the sensing of a physical influence of some single form of energy and its recoding as the primary code of information;

2. modeling of portions of the information in the form of a temporary model;

3. a program of comparison of the temporary model with models of permanent standards — the selection of information of a higher level; and

4. the memory of a new model in the form of a structure which is made from a sequence of models in terms of the symbols of a new code.

In very complex systems, as in man, there are other programs for the reproduction of cortical models in the form of physical ones — of things, of drawings, of letters.

The stamp of subjectivity is evident at all stages of the creation of a system model: The model reflects programs of both the object and of the subject. As a matter of fact, every transducer generally senses one form of energy which it selects from the total influence of the object, ignoring other, possibly even more important ones. Recoding this energy in terms of a primary code takes place according to nonlinear functions and besides this it depends upon the state of the subject. All other levels of modeling are likewise changeable — the program of comparison, the standards of symbols of the new code, and the programs for the reproduction of models. This relates equally well to both natural and to artificial modeling systems.

There can be wide differences in the degree to which a model is similar to the original. One evaluates this degree of similarity by the selection of other models of information concerning the system. Thus, for example, a drawing of a steamship made by a child is quite far from the original, but drafts and other technological documentation, reproduce the vessel in exact detail and allow for the manufacture of a new copy of the vessel.

To the extent that programs for the creation of models may differ, to that extent it is possible to reflect every system by any number of such programs. In reality, sense organs or transducers select various forms of primary information as a function of the form of the sensed energy (radiation, air waves). The character of the transducers (of the receptors) defines the character of the primary models. The processing of primary information according to different programs (comparing it with different systems of codes-standards) will in turn yield a multitude of hierarchical models. Furthermore; at higher levels an integration of information obtained from different primary codes (sight, hearing) is possible, this in time or in space, resulting in the creation of unified composite models. The quantity of possible models and the degree of their correspondence with the object is directly determined by programs of modeling-cognition, programs which are inherent to the modeling mechanism — to the subject. For example, different models are formed, in the cerebral cortex of a person who is examining some item — models of its light, color, form, mobility, dimensions, other properties, names, associations with other systems, and so forth.

Models are quite varied in their structure. Since they reflect only one or, at best, several codes of the information transmitted by the system or its programs, there may be no similarity between the model and object (provided we understand the similarity as simply being of the visual image).

Models can be separated into two large groups: a) models in natural modeling systems — images; and b) physical models made by man.

The former group can be imagined simply as images which are stored in the cerebral cortex. These are structures of nerve cells connected by conductors with "well-worn" synapses. However, such identification is far from complete. Every living system, having a multileveled structure, is capable of generating information, that is, of creating models. Models of the external influence are created in any cell — perhaps in a primitive form, being reflected in the dynamics of the change of its frequency. Even with a minimal degree of similarity with an external factor, its reflection will be a model at least to the degree that it will provoke a change in the living functions of the cell.

Each level of complex systems has its own types of models. In the cell they are expressed by structures made from molecules; in the complex organism, by structures made from cells; and in society, by physical models; books, things. The second type of model is of particular interest.

Man employs different means for the creation of physical models or more correctly, for the reproduction of his own cortical models. Let us enumerate these:

1. Description with words. This is a universal form which is suitable for the reproduction of a model at any level and of any primary code of energy. One can describe sight and sound images: their detailed characteristic makes up the lower-level code, a re-telling of the contents or only of the idea is a higher-level code. However, in all cases, similarity of the model to the original will be quite relative and the degree of subjectivity will be great.

2. Drawings, drafts. The possibilities of this code are limited by visual models, that is, by the sensing of light energy and the production of models from it. Usually this is a lower-level code since attempts to represent meaning separate from form has not been crowned with success. The spectator locates the meaning and does this very subjectively.

3. Physical models. Their diversity is great — from simple reproduction of form and spatial relations up to expression by completely different (from the subject) physical elements of sep-arate programs of the object.

4. Mathematical models are a description of purely informa-tional functions with the help of different "mathematical" standards: numbers, formulas, equations, systems of equations. These are exact models under specific limited conditions. It does not, how-ever, appear possible to describe very complex systems mathe-matically: it is difficult to obtain exact relationships and it is difficult to coordinate different programs. Furthermore, pre-paring a mathematical expression of a program and finding the solution of complex mathematical problems where the aim is to find the concrete parameters of a system under given conditions demands a great deal of time. In general, this was impossible up to the appearance of electronic computers.

5. Models created with the help of computers. These deserve particular attention. In essence, mathematical models are reflected in computers in manifest form as in the case where prepared equa-tions are programmed or in nonmanifest form wherein only functions between separate "pieces" of exact mathematical pro-grams are stored in the program. One way or another, electronic computers allow for obtaining large, precise, or approximate models of separate programs of very complex systems, something which could not have been attained by other means — by codes.

6. Very complex physical models of separate programs of a system-object are created by contemporary electronic means since parameters of electric current can very conveniently simulate parameters of complex systems which are expressed in terms of other physical units. Electronic simulating mechanisms in the form

of standard machines or special mechanisms, as distinguished from all other means, allows the creation of an "operating" model of a system in which a program of its changes in time is clearly expressed and can be utilized for cognition and control. Undoubtedly, this is the highest type of physical model.

Any simulating mechanism has limits to its capabilities (limit of cognition), which is determined by its structure, by the quantity and diversity of the elements and of their connections. Modeling (cognizing) a system of great complexity, the limited mechanism is capable of reproducing either a simplified general model of the system, or comparatively detailed models of some particular programs or structures. The modeling mechanism does not have the capacity to simulate in a detailed way a system which is more complicated than itself. For example, in the human organism it has been calculated that there are 10,000 billion cells. The cerebral cortex is a modeling system which is composed of from 10-14 billion cells. Of course man's brain, even with the very best utilization of its cells cannot create a detailed model of the entire organism. If we consider that modeling of the organisms must begin not from cells but from molecules out of which the cells are constructed, then attempts at cognition of the organism with the help of the brain appear clearly unsound. The cortex can model in a generalized way only the higher levels of programs of man and is capable of reproducing in detail only models of its component parts.

Consequently, we should note that the limit of complexity of the cognitive systems imposed by the modeling mechanism depends not only on the number of elements entering into its composition; no less important is the structure of their combinations which determines the program of modeling. First of all, the structure designates the capability for generating models at higher levels and also the total quantity of diverse models which determine the qualities of a system as a function of the presence of codes-qualities.

Considering what has been said one can speak about the following possibilities, or limits of the modeling mechanism:

1. The magnitude of the cognitive systems — understanding by this the total capacity of retained information on some lower level. In other words: the limiting magnitude of a system which one can remember, that is, modeling its structure; for example, the limiting size of a schematic of a complex eletrical grid or a simple quantity of facts which belong to one or more systems. The preceding relates to both lower levels and to any higher level of information. If we return once more to the example, then this is not only the volume of literally remembered texts of books (lower level) but also the number of books whose contents are remembered (a higher level).

2. The limit of capability for the generation of models at higher levels, or the capability to "understand the meaning" of programs of complex systems. In accordance with a general program for the

generation of hierarchical models, it is necessary to recall a temporary model of the sensed influence (or of the information) and to compare this model with models of standards of symbols of a code. It is known that the higher the level the greater the quantity of symbols in the alphabet of possible symbols. Consequently, a modeling mechanism capable of "understanding meaning," must have a much greater memory than a mechanism which simply recalls primary or lower-level information.   There are people who are called "walking encyclopedias" who nevertheless do not contribute anything to knowledge since they do not have programs for the generation of higher-level meaning from the information which is stored in their memory.

Of course, in speaking of the generation of higher semantic models, I mean the capability to generate many models-qualities, and not just a single "higher meaning."

3. The limit of speed of sensing and information processing. This depends on all links of the system — on programs of receptors which sense physical influence, recoding it by a lower-level informational code, on programs for the generation of higher-level models. "Rapidly operating" machines depend on their programs in addition to the operation of their elements. Thus, for example, an electronic computer requires more time than an experienced doctor for the formulation of a diagnosis for heart disease although the speed of the computer is unmatched by physiological speeds.

Let us now consider the question of the completeness of understanding (the modeling) of some system. It would appear that the ultimate in completeness of modeling of a system is the creation of a duplicate new system having the very same structure and, consequently, the very same programs. This, however, is not completely so.   To begin with, it is practically impossible to create a system *identical* with the system to be modeled in the simplest case of machine duplication.   On some lower level, the copies will still be distinguishable by the structure of the molecules, atoms, and even elementary particles.   Although these differences will prove to be only secondary from the point of view of execution of *main* programs, that is, the basic operation, these differences will be manifest in something else — in the longevity of operation under the unusual conditions. In practice, every modeling must begin from some lower level: when applied to an organism, from the level of organs, cells, molecules, out of which these organisms are constructed.   It is difficult to imagine a modeling apparatus which creates a system in duplicate, beginning from the level of atoms or of elementary particles.

The upper level of modeling must be contemplated in a similar manner. In reality, any given system, no matter how independent it may appear, is a part, an element, of other higher-level systems. Its life, behavior, concrete (but not its possible) programs depend not only on its particular structure but also on the higher level and neighboring systems. Consequently, in order to model a systems future, it is necessary to know both its structure at each given moment and all influences which await it in the future and which of these will alter this structure and thus its subsequent programs. Let us consider such an example. The modeling of a microbe beginning from the level of molecules apparently exhibits all of its programs: nutrition, reproduction, capacity for adaptation to the changing external environment. These programs continue even after division of the cell. However, is it possible to guess the fate of its future generations? Perhaps they will perish from some detrimental conditions or they will adapt to them by virtue of their inherent changeability. Possibly a cosmic particle will enter into the DNA of one of the daughter cells and a new type of microbe will arise. We cannot know all of this by studying the microbial cell alone. Its structure at a given moment allows us to determine only possible programs and not actual programs — those which are realized as a consequence of the influence of external conditions, that is, of higher-level systems. One cannot forget the thesis: structure is all possible programs. From these programs only one is realized — is activated by the influences. As a result of the execution of the first program, the structure will have changed and, consequently, so will the programs which follow.

Therefore every modeling (cognition) is only probabilistic. Such models yield to computation, although, here again, the computation is not exact.

Every cognition follows some goals and by these goals a range of programs is determined which must be modeled. These will include main programs, and a series of other programs on which these depend.

Main programs are generally higher-level programs of the behavior of the entire system. However, it does not follow, that they are main for the cognitive system. Thus, for a dermatologist, who studies and treats different skin diseases, programs for the disturbance of life of cells of the skin are the main programs. Even when simply investigating something out of curiosity an individual will set narrower goals for himself and occupy himself with the general investigation.

Since it is impossible to model all lower- and higher-level programs of a system, their scope must be limited as a function of the established goals. Furthermore, it is always necessary to first take into account that the models obtained will be probabilistic and not exact. The question concerns the degree of their accuracy. Here everything depends on the object and the specificity of those of its programs which it presumably models and of course on the modeling possibilities of the subject. The point is that the degree of independence of different programs varies in different systems. Some subsystems (structures) which ensure the execution of a certain program, may be very closely associated with other structures, therefore their programs as a whole depend on neighboring ones. This may take the form of a synergism, of a coordination, or of noise. Thus, programs of activity of the intestines depends to a large degree on influences from regulatory systems and the stomach, and the heart as an organ possesses a significant degree of independence.

In order to obtain reliable models of some single program of a complex system, it is necessary either to isolate the corresponding structure, its vehicle, or to simultaneously model those neighboring higher- and lower-level programs which exert influence on this program. If a system is very complex it may be impossible to do this within the limitations of the modeling apparatus, thus an alternative approach is required. One may reproduce the modeled program within limits accessible to the cognizing system and to present all the remaining programs in the form of noises which are statistically modeled. Of course, in doing this accuracy suffers, but unfortunately there is no alternative.

Returning to the question of completeness of modeling, we must note that the greatest volume of information is contained in detailed models on a lower level. As has already been indicated, a multitude of higher-level models can be produced from any available program of information processing. However, it does not follow from this that lower-level detailed models are basic for cognition of a complex system. Connected phrases when recorded on tape are just such a detailed model but without generation of higher-meaning models, these are of little value for the sensing and understanding of speech. Therefore, with regard to the goal of understanding (cognition) some optimal mix and connection of models of lower and higher levels is indispensable.

For example, in order to understand a disease such as heart disease, there is no need to descend to modeling at the molecular level of the cellular exchange since a description of programs of operation of the entire heart as a hydromechanical system provides sufficient data for an opinion concerning the pathology. It is another matter if we wish to arbitrarily control the operation of the heart. For this it is necessary to know the intimate biochemical processes of its muscular fibers and conducting system in order to plan influences on these in the necessary direction. With respect to another disease, such as cancer, we simply cannot manage without modeling at the molecular level of the cells since it is evident that the reason for this illness is in disturbances of the program for cell division and that the vehicles of this program are DNA molecules — the controlling system of the cells.

Consider another example. For the creation of an automatic machine which can act as an artificial "thinking" system, it is sufficient to simulate the higher programs of behavior and thinking of man. With knowledge of these programs it is possible to construct such new structures from elements completely different from nerve cells. But to recreate a living person, models would be required at many levels since it would be necessary to reproduce the "technology" of synthesis of complex molecular and cellular structures.

Thus, the possibilities for modeling the human brain are limited. It is not possible to understand complex systems with the exhaustive completeness necessary for their control or for their reproduction. It is true that these possibilities were significantly broadened from the moment of formation of a new higher-level system — that of human society. Up to that time, the cerebral cortex of man was employed most insufficiently. In all probability this is still the case. Certainly it is possible to greatly increase the modeling possibilities of the cortex by early education and training.

When man first learned to reproduce his cortical models in terms of things, that is, to create artificial physical systems, new perspectives for understanding of the world were revealed. The development of writing strongly promoted this. Words—recorded letters — became models which possess their own "life." Books are things which serve as a means for the accumulation of models for society and the means for education of society's new members. Furthermore, with the aid of books and other things, man broadens his own memory, saving his thoughts-models from the inevitable forgetting. It is true that in order to utilize these models at a later date it is necessary to again reestablish through repetition that information which has already been assimilated, but, on the other hand, this readily activates the old models in memory which, generally speaking, are never completely erased. Books and things created civilization since these ensured the possibility of collective cognition and continuity in the development of knowledge.

However, these items do not fully resolve the problem of the limited modeling capacity of the brain. A collection of people with modern means for data manipulation still are unable to create complete models of very complex systems. Let us try to understand why.

When a problem concerning a very complex system having many programs is presented to a group of scientists (as, for example, that of a living organism), then it is completely logical to proceed with a division of labor. Some study the cells, determining by means of some "external" codes how these interact. Other scientists occupy themselves with organs in which the cellular flow of information is integrated and "organ flows" of information are created. A third group formulates models of systems of organs (for example, that of the cardiovascular or nervous system). Finally, someone integrates the "system" information and obtains models of the behavior of the entire organism. Engineers would begin to work in about this same way if they found it necessary to study some complex technical apparatus (such as, an electric power station) without the aid of technical documentation. In practice, this is the very way in which they operate, creating complex constructions such as the plan for a large ship or for a factory. The volume of information in such cases is so great that one man cannot embrace it, but it is manageable by a group of designers. Unfortunately, the simplest living cell is more complex than any technological system, to say nothing about organisms such as the higher animals and man. It is because of this very fact that the success of medical doctors and biologists in the creation of theory has been so limited. There is a fantastically large number of closely associated elements and subsystems in the living organism. The flow of information goes not only from "below to above," that is, from cells to the entire organism, but also from "above to below" — from higher levels to lower ones. The behavior of the entire organism is the result of the integration of particular cellular programs, however, even the conditions for the existence of cells is directly dependent on the behavior of the entire organism, as, for example, in hunger or overwork.

To understand the organism, it is necessary to create a working model of it which would reflect at least the main connections and dependencies if not all such relations. And this must be done in a quantitative form as it is done in technology. By means of description it is impossible to achieve this. Scientists have, in general, established possible connections between structures and their programs of activity; however, until these data acquire quantitative expression, it will be impossible to evaluate their significance. Until the separate weight of various regulating systems becomes clear from the execution of programs of various functional acts or pathological processes, attempts will continue to generate all possible universal theories of medicine, on the order of the cortical hypothesis of Bikov or the endocrine theory of Selye.

Considering the great complexity of living systems, it is difficult to imagine the possibility for the creation of an entire model of the organism similar to, say, a plan for an electric power station. However, making use of exact methods of investigation and taking a mathematical approach in the study of phenomena can significantly increase the precision of the available descriptive model. But even with this, models do not gain the detail necessary for reproduction (the creation) of new organisms. Even the possibility for control remains limited in that some programs, such as those concerned with aging, demand modeling at the molecular level.

New technological means are necessary for the modeling of extremely complex systems. Simulation machines of the future will provide such means.

Even now at the contemporary level of development of computer technology, electronic computers can solve scientific and practical problems which were not previously accessible to man. The very fact that a large volume of information can be processed within a limited time not only simplifies the execution of the technological operation, but also allows for finding new dependencies; dependencies which would have been impossible to discover using the old methods of "hand" processing of material.

Unfortunately, the very principle of operation of contemporary computers places limits on the complexity of the problems which are being solved by them. The following are inherent deficiencies of these machines:

1. Programs of machines are of a linear character. That is, at any given moment impulses move sequentially from one element to the next and all other models from memory do not participate in the activity.   In other words, in the machine, only one program is executed. It can be very long and complex in the sense of number of switchings, but all these operations are executed sequentially.

Natural complex systems — living organisms function in a completely different way. In these systems a huge number, literally millions of programs, are realized simultaneously. At any given moment a significant portion of the structural elements participate in these programs.   The information is immediately reprocessed along many parallel paths at different levels. Although the speed of information processing in the organism is very low in comparison with that of electronic computers, the volume of information simultaneously reprocessed in the organism exceeds by many times that of even the most complex and rapid electronic computer.   The linear construction of programs in machines greatly encumbers the selection of required data, since in the search for these it is necessary to examine all the reprocessed information.

2. In contemporary machines there are "narrow" places which lower the effectiveness of their operation.   Apart from the comparative slowness of selection of necessary data from the external memory, the speeds of input and output of information are quite low.   The most significant deficiency of machines, which again follows from the basic principle of their activity, is the extreme complexity of their hierarchical information processing. Obtaining models at higher levels demands so much calculation that the effectiveness of machines is depreciated.   Even such a comparatively simple problem as the discrimination of images is only solved with difficulty. The very selection of general and abstract concepts meets indefinable obstacles at the present time.

3. Simulation of complex programs in machines presents great difficulties to programmers because it requires the conversion of hierarchical (volume) models into linear ones.

4. Contemporary machines are cumbersome and insufficiently reliable in operation. Insofar as the program is "drawn out in one line," a breakdown of even one element will lead to shutdown of the entire machine.

These enumerated deficiencies are very serious, however, they are completely surmountable. Achievements of the last few years demonstrate this. Methods for the compilation of programs are rapidly being perfected. There are already general "programs for compilation of programs" — their original higher-level code. Methods are now being developed for parallel information processing according to several programs. Finally, new small elements, and schematics built of these, are being created which possess high reliability owing to the utilization of parallel and standby redundancy.

Electronic and computer technology is developing rapidly. Without doubt, in the near future well-developed informational systems will be created, systems which will be capable of exceeding the limits of the human brain.

For successful development of this work, it is very important to attempt to uncover programs of information processing by man even if only at the higher levels, in other words, expressed in a general form and not related to concrete cellular structures of the cortex and subcortex.

2

The Evolution of Pre-Human Living
Systems and Their Programs

Any developing system may be considered in two ways: physical and informational. In the former, we attempt to understand the physical essence of processes which occur within the system, which change it in time, and which exert influence on other systems. In the latter, we limit ourselves to a description of the general regularities of changes of the system, basing these on changes of some external characteristics or of their composite, this being observed in time and space.

Of course, in both the physical and informational sense we are studying the system, that is, we are constructing its model. The difference is purely quantitative: a physical plan requires a detailed model beginning at the lowest possible level — atoms or molecules. In studying systems in an informational way, modeling begins directly with programs at higher levels without any concern for the essence of the systems basic physical processes.

Of course, a physical plan is more complete and more valuable. However, one must consider the possibilities of the modeling system. For example, to understand a cell it is best to model all the atoms, the molecules, and their connections which comprise the system. Then the cell behavior will be completely comprehensible — cellular exchange, movement, reproduction, disease. Nevertheless, for the time being, this approach is beyond our capabilities. Therefore, we must begin modeling from a higher level — from the activity of the cell as a unit.

As indicated above, there are various interrelationships between levels of programs in complex systems. Any particular program, higher-level programs included, may be more or less dependent on neighboring or lower-level programs. Since in an informational way it is sufficient to model only a part of the system program for its description, the relative value of the obtained models will be determined by the dependence of a given program on those which have not entered the model. Furthermore, the goal is important. If the goal is to study the physiology of the brain we cannot limit ourselves to a description of the external signs of the animals behavior. If we undertake the construction of a robot, intended to execute a series of animal or human operating functions, the informational approach will yield all that we need.

General laws of development of living systems. In an informational sense these laws are well-understood by science. The two laws are mutation and natural selection. Recently, models of the physical aspect of both programs have been outlined: the structure of DNA has been deciphered and it has been shown that all qualities of the future organism are encoded in this structure. It is true that this still leaves us far from a "particular" model — from a map of characteristics and programs of their formation. It is quite possible that the human brain is unable to cope with this task and by default will relegate it to computers. However, this is a problem for the future.

The struggle for existence proceeds chiefly in the macroworld and is, therefore, quite accessible to study. But for a quantitative expression, for comprehension of this extremely complex and varied process, a powerful modeling facility is required.

Mutations are changes in DNA caused by physical or chemical influences (primarily by cosmic radiation). Thus, these changes are in the physical plan. The simpler the organism, the greater its alterability, for in a comparatively simple program of development useful changes are more easily realized. The consequences of this alterability are more easily manifested: simple organisms have a brief life and reproduction is intensive.

The more complex the organism, the more difficult it is to change its structure. The program for the formation of an advanced animal or of man is very complex and disturbance of its model leads to such sharp contradictions between components that the progeny lack vitality in the vast majority of cases. "Successful" mutations for advanced organisms are highly improbable. It is difficult to understand how such a complex and purposeful world developed considering the contemporary mutation frequency. In all probability, cosmic radiation was more intense in the remote past and therefore mutations occurred with greater frequency.

Transmission of acquired characteristics is still possible in plants or simple animals where, distances between operating structures and those in which the hereditary information is stored is not great. However, with respect to advanced animals this concept is completely inappropriate; as, for example, where hypertrophy of some group of muscles following exercises will result in an alteration of the DNA in the sex cells.

In the process of change, organisms are created accidentally — "without plan." Therefore, it does not follow that all of their structures and, consequently, their programs are mutually coordinated. On the contrary, many contradictions may remain between them. On the whole, there is successful coordination, but in details — contradictions occur.

Usually, systems become complex because the connections between previously existing elements are consolidated and not because of the formation of new elements. Multicellular organisms developed because of changes in the hereditary structures which resulted in firm connections between daughter cells derived from the dividing one-celled organism. Human society as a durable system is a result of reinforcement of the connections between people. Consequently, with the development of a system at a new level of complexity, the preserved partial programs of the elements which enter into it are only somewhat modified by the new conditions of existence and, therefore, do not always correspond to new programs of the entire organism. In this we find the second contradiction of complex systems — the contradiction between levels.

Systems are created not only as a result of direct mutation, as when a structure of an organism is changed, but as a result of modified programs of external activity as well. The latter entails change of relations between existing organisms: old organizations are dissolved and new more advance ones are created.

Basic programs of a complex system. As we have said, the concept of "system" is relative. Creation of a system entails elements and connections — interactions. Systems are distinguished from the "general world" on the basis of quantitative evaluation of the stability of the connections, or the strength of interaction between their parts.

The cell of a complex organism is a system having molecules as its elements. A multicellular organism is a system of cells. The family, the species, is a very simple system of organisms, a system associated with the acts of its members. We can also consider a biological form to be a system consisting of primary cells — of families, of species (connections within it are quite weak and are only distinguished artificially). Living creatures which inhabit some geographical territory (such as an island) are again a system, although this system is composed of completely heterogeneous elements. In the final analysis, all life on earth may be considered as a system.

A system is a structure. A structure is a set of programs. In every system, complex or simple, programs of its lower-level systems are stored as are programs of the higher-level systems in which the system is embedded. These programs may be distinguished more or less accurately. Let us consider them in a most general way:

1. Fundamental programs — "for one's self." The "life of a system" embraces a complex of total programs which in their realization ensure the possibility of self-preservation, to save

the system from dissolution. For example, for an animal, these are instincts with all the involved reflexes, and for society these are the relations between people.

2. Lower-level programs are fundamental programs of elements or of parts of a system. Ultimately, the total programs of the system are constructed from these. However, as a condition of this, a strictly determined structure of the parts is essential.

3. Higher programs ensure the existence and "life" of an advanced system, in which the "given" comprises only a part. There may be several such programs depending on the quantity of levels of the advanced system as specified in the given data.

The following examples will illustrate this. A cell in a complex organism has its fundamental programs — "for one's self" — for itself as an individual. This amounts to the obtaining of energy from nutritive materials, the synthesis of new structures, defense (for example, in the form of chemical reactions which immobilize poisons). Lower programs lead to particular chemical changes in cellular molecular structures, such as in the nucleus, organelles, membrane. Higher programs can be represented in two levels. Reproduction of a cell constitutes the program "for the species": for the tissue, for the organ. The specific activity (for example, contraction of volume or the nerve impulses) is made up of programs necessary for the higher system — for the organism. These programs are completely unnecessary for the cell itself. Structures which provide for specific activity atrophy in a culture, that is, when they are external to the organism: under these conditions a cell survives only by its own "animal" life and reproduces only for continuation of the species.

Man provides us with a different example. His programs "for one's self" are represented by the instinct of self-preservation (nutrition, defense) associated with higher levels of the cerebral cortex. Programs of the next higher system, whether the family or species, are instincts for continuation of the species: sexual, parental. Finally, programs of a still higher system, "society" ("species") represent a complex of cortical programs which determine human behavior. On the other hand, the human organism also has programs of lower systems, of internal organs.

As has been indicated, we can divide the development of complex systems into three levels: single-celled systems in which diversity is attained, by molecular combinations; multicellular systems — up to man — involves an integration of the diversity of molecules and the diversity of cells. The third level is represented by human society or by species of animals, combining the diversity of structures of molecules, cells, and organisms. Regardless of the level of the system, it will contain all types of programs — "for one's self," "for the family," and "for the species." Each of these is represented by different structural levels which provide for the hierarchical construction of programs. A bacterium, for example, is a structure at the first level, but has all three program types, that of the individual, of the family, and of the species. Man belongs to systems at the second level. He has the same three types of multileveled programs, but they are many times more complex than those in bacteria. Every program includes sensing and processing of the obtained information and a modeling of information imparted.

A system as a whole is characterized by the quantity and hierarchy of its programs, that is, by the diversity of its structure.

The general direction of progress has been toward the formation of more complex systems: their level is raised and the quantity of levels increases within the limits of each. For example, a cell of a mammal is much more complex than the cell of the simplest unicellular organism. A biological species is a system at a third level. However, in quantity and hierarchy of programs, human society stands incomparably higher than, let us say, the wolf pack or the ant colony.

The behavior of a system is determined by its highest level. Nevertheless, this level remains closely associated with lower levels. It models the lower levels, influences them, and is itself subjected to influence and change.

The basic stages of evolution. We will discuss in greater detail, programs of living organisms relative to their evolution, but limiting ourselves to the informational aspects. Hence, it seems appropriate to isolate the following stages of development of living systems:

1. primary molecules;
2. unicellular organisms;
3. multicellular organisms below the level of development of a cerebral cortex; and
4. multicellular organisms having a cerebral cortex, excluding man.

The appearance of each of the above systems meant the appearance of new programs, qualitatively distinct from previous ones.

I will not delve into theories concerning the origin of life on earth. Many renowned scholars (Oparin and others) have treated this subject sufficiently. Evidently, several variants of the initial complex "living" molecule were possible. The first variant: "living" molecules were formed from simpler organic molecules under favorable conditions and were destroyed under unfavorable conditions. The fact is that the program of life consists of a molecular combination process. Probably one cannot call these living since they do not reproduce. A second variant: after forming, a complex molecule "lives" if it reproduces, that is, if it by itself creates similar molecules provided conditions are sufficiently propitious in that suitable simple molecules are available. However, life even in this case is not a necessary result. In the absence of favorable conditions, the molecule may be inactive and behave as any other stable molecule of simple inorganic or organic composition.

Viruses are illustrative examples. They consist of molecules of DNA, surrounded by protein molecules. They reproduce only after penetration of a living cell that provides the necessary conditions for doubling of the DNA and the creation of new proteins. A virus outside of a living organism is simply a conglomeration of complex molecules, crystal-like, and does not show signs of life. Of course, viruses cannot be considered as the primary "living" molecules from which life on earth originated. It is possible, that they are descendants of earlier primary forms and have adapted to a world of complex living creatures as parasitic forms.

Thus, primary "living" molecules have two combined programs — nutrition and reproduction. The first is "for one's self" and the second is "for the family and for the species." The code of information obtained consists of simple molecules, of information imparted — that of a single complex ("living") molecule.

A program for the modeling of one's self begins at the molecular state and is similar to that which occurs with DNA of viruses. A long DNA molecule, under specified conditions, is divided along its longitudinal axis and each half builds itself up at the expense of free nucleotides.

Of course, there is a still lower level of program in which atoms and their elements participate. Only by these can the mechanism of destruction of some connections and the creation of others be explained.

Unicellular organisms in nature are generally represented by microorganisms. Although considered the simplest, they are in reality highly organized structures which possess correspondingly complex programs. We can distinguish at least two types among the latter: programs "for one's self" — nutrition, movement, defense, and "for family and species" — reproduction. Each has a hierarchical structure adapted for the generation of different codes of information and for the corresponding planning of operations. In all probability, three levels of programs and correspondingly, of codes of information, may be distinguished (Fig. 3).

The first level is that of operating programs. These can be reduced to the following basic forms:

1. Nutrition, that is, processes of seizing and decomposition of nutritive materials with the liberation of energy or the formation of particles suitable for assimilation.

2. Defense, expressed primarily in rendering poisonous materials harmless and also in resisting harmful physical agents.

3. Movement, that is, the change of form under the influence of external and internal stimuli.

All these programs are realized according to the general principles of chemical transformations; fixation (sensing) of the first substance is a symbol of a lower code, its accumulation within specified limits (temporary memory), comparison with a matrix-standard corresponds to a conversion into a new substance — is a symbol of a new, higher-level code. As a result, the first model — the accumulation of the first substance — disappears. Symbols of the higher code, the new substance, may accumulate and form a new model of the external influence.

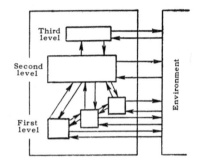

FIG. 3. Schematic of cellular programs. First level - programs of working reactions, interconnected by direct and reverse connections.   Second level - plastic reactions, which realize processes of adaptation by way or regulation of working reactions of a lower level. In the third level, programs of reproduction and hereditary information are stored. Each level can have connections with the external environment which stimulate or inhibit appropriate reactions.

All transformations within living cells are realized by means of enzymes and occur in special structures — in simulating subsystems of the cell. Specific values for the speed of the reactions depend on the character of external stimuli. Usually, these reactions are self-regulating, having internal feedback. Separate programs are interconnected by transverse connections in some general "economy."

A second level realizes the regulation of the first as a function of the slow changes of the external world which are not caught by the first brief-memory level. In general, the second level realizes reactions of adaptation, amplifies some functions, weakens others, changes values of the magnitude of the effect due to the strength of the stimulus; in other words, changes the characteristics of the first-level processes.

With this goal, the second level generates different models of information from the rapidly changing external influences sensed by the first level. Generation of several codes are possible: according to the sum, speed, acceleration, to the correlation between different stimuli. The principle of generation of information is the usual one — sensing, temporary memory, comparison with standards of the symbols of the code, production of a new symbol.   Accumulation of information in memory is possible — models of the symbols of a new code.

Besides the program of information processing on the second level, there is the program of influences — the model of programs of a second level.   Its essence lies in the change of speed of the chemical reactions of the first, working level.   In living cells, the second level is represented in the form of the RNA which synthesizes proteins—enzymes for working chemical reactions.   The speed of synthesis is determined by a nonlinear dependence on the availability of the enzyme, which, in turn is determined by its expenditure in the process of execution of the reactions elicited by the external influences.   Enzymes are the code of information produced by the second level of the cell.

A third level of cellular structures is the nucleus which, in principle, must generate a higher level of information — models of still slower changes of the external world.   It may well be that in the nucleus there are molecules of DNA which synthesize RNA for the second level.   It is improper to view the function of the nucleus as being solely reproductive, for it also participates in the "ordinary" life of the cell, although not uniformly.   It is known that a cell will perish several weeks after removal of the nucleus.

Thus, in programs "for one's self" a third level regulates processes of the second level, generating higher codes of information.   However, the chief function of the third level is that of realizing programs for reproduction — a program "for the family and species."   Of course, it does not follow that this whole program is stored only here. The program has its second and first levels, since processes of growth of the cell, structural changes and exchanges in the course of division occur just as a result of its realization.   But, nevertheless this is a separate program, distinct from ordinary activity.

Activation of the reproduction program, as that of any other program, is realized by a signal.   There is an accumulation of some structures during growth — that is, a storage of information.   The moment of maturity of the cell is registered by a feedback system which signals this point to a higher level — to the nucleus.   In response to the signal, programs of reproduction are activated in the nucleus, programs of structural perturbations resulting in the formation of two daughter cells from one old cell. This program is rigid to the degree that the cell has all that is necessary for its realization at the beginning of the action.

One can formulate several general properties of programs of one-celled organisms.

1. Modeling of the external world is realized because of molecular structures, and this possibly within quite tight limits. The quantity of sensed influences (forms of energy and substances) is small and correspondingly the possibilities for generation of the

higher-level codes (change in time, combinations) are insignificant. Consequently, adaptability to changes of the external world is low and the degree of accuracy of the models is also low.

2. The number of programs of a cell is small. They are basically of significant rigidity, of few levels, and offer limited possibilities for self-regulation.

3. The programs "for one's self" are weak and do not provide for high survivability. This is compensated for by intensive reproduction, that is, by the program "for the family and for the species."

4. Limited adaptability of the individual to change of the external conditions is compensated for by significant alterability — due to frequent mutations and possibly due to the inheritance of acquired characteristics. Frequent "success" of mutations is accounted for by the relative simplicity of the reproduction and growth program, disturbance of which is rarely accompanied by insurmountable contradictions between the components of the structure, as occurs in complex mammals.

5. Codes of external information differ for various types of programs. Movement, generation of chemical substances (both in the form of a few specific complexes in time) are the code for the program "for one's self"; new progeny are the code for programs "for the family and for the species."

Formation of multicellular noncortical organisms during evolution also occurred as a result of mutation. Certain changes in the DNA structure resulted in incomplete division of unicellular organisms, the daughter cells remained together and exerted significant influence on each other. With time, their program of reproduction and growth became exceedingly complex, leading finally to the generation of multicellular organisms with specialized cells. It is difficult to imagine how DNA in the chromosome of the embryonic cell can be imprinted with the smallest of details for the construction of every cell of a complex organism down to the molecular level. We must assume that the program for development is hierarchical, is rigid, but with feedbacks which activate new links as the execution of previous links proceeds. For every newly formed cell, programs of working reactions and programs of reproduction are separately formulated in the complex of the entire organism. Feedback stops reproduction once specific quantitative relations have been attained.

Multicellular organisms belong to systems at a second level and therefore their programs must be distinguished as cellular and total.

Cells in a complex organism have the same three types of programs as the organism in its entirety:

1. "For one's self" there are working reactions of basic exchange, energy supply, defense against harmful agents. These programs are closely interconnected and have the same three levels and programs of a unicellular organism.

2. "For the family" there are programs of growth and reproduction, also at three levels.

3. "For the organism" (of a higher system) there are programs of specialized activity. An example of such activity is the contraction of a muscle cell, the transmission of nerve impulses or secretions of hormones by endocrine cells. These activities are not required for the cell itself. The cell merely executes assignments of the organism, submitting to specific organismic influences. Programs of specialized activity developed from elements of programs "for one's self": contractions — from the movements of the unicellular organism due to its contractile elements; hormones or something similar were necessary to the cell itself for control of its own separate programs. These simple programs changed in the direction of greater effectiveness and control, as a rule to the detriment of some other programs of the complex "for one's self."

Through its own regulating systems, consisting of specialized cells, the organism can influence any level of all cellular programs. Nevertheless, cells preserve some independence — this being different under different circumstances. Even programs of reproduction which are severely blocked by integrated influences, in some instances become disobedient and develop into tumors.

Programs of the whole organism are determined by the structure of cells and their specialized activity. We can classify these according to the very same three types:

1. "For one's self" — nutrition, defense.

2. "For the family" — correlation of the first and second program which together ensure the species potentials in the struggle for survival.

Each of these programs can be further divided into two components which closely interact — into an external and internal subprogram. The first of these determines the influences on the surrounding world. Its basic code is movement and to a lesser degree, chemical secretion. The second subprogram embraces the interactions between internal organs and their cells, ensuring useful muscular activity. The codes of internal subprograms take the form of chemicals of great diversity.

All programs and their components are hierarchical. Structures from specialized cells form levels where entering information is processed and the produced information is modeled. The number of levels depends on the degree of complexity of the animal. The levels of the external programs are interconnected with a strict subordination that ensures at any given moment the execution of only one and the suppression of the remainder. Internal programs are exceedingly varied, proceed in parallel, and have a significant degree of autonomy.

The most advanced level of all the enumerated programs is that of instinct. There are two instincts: that of self-preservation (component programs are "nutrition" and "defense") and continuation of the family (component programs are "reproduction" and "training," in other words, sexual and parental instincts). Models of these programs are stored in the internal sphere, in cells of regulating systems, that is, the endocrine and nervous systems.   They are activated from the external environment (defense) or from the internal environment (hunger, sexual feeling).   Lower levels are represented by different unconditional reflexes and cellular reactions.

All models of reflexes and instincts are rather rigid, their structures are innate.   They are intended to provide a reaction to specific external environmental influences — as in automata. Adaptability to changes in the external world, in the form of conditioned reflexes, is ensured by the redundant connections between nerve cells in the rigid structures and by programs of cellular adaptation, in particular, the hypertrophy and adaptation of the cells.   However, the alternatives of both these mechanisms is limited, as is the time of adaptation.   The experience of biologists has demonstrated that conditioned reflexes can be developed in noncortical animals and even among unicellular organisms, though the latter is accomplished only within very narrow limits and only after a huge number of combinations of stimuli have been provided for the formation of the reflex, this in the order of thousands or more.

The complexity of rigid innate structures is sharply increased with increase in the volume of information processed, with increase of diversity of the motor acts, and with their continuation in time. In other words, with rigid programs an innate structure is related to each external stimulus.   Only the possibility of envisaging a multitude of different external conditions and, consequently, the availability of a multitude of structure-programs ensures great adaptability.   The number of combinations of external stimuli which require special programs increases in proportion to the square of the number of separate influences. It follows that with rigid programs it is very difficult to ensure flexibility of adaptation to diverse and constantly changing external influences. The survivability of these comparatively primitive species can be explained by high fertility or by the availability of specific powerful defense mechanisms or offense mechanisms.

In the course of the emergence and change of new species, nature has created exceptional structural diversity and consequently great diversity of programs — and thus still at a level of the lower noncortical animals.   It is impossible to survey all of them. I will attempt to categorize and characterize them only in an informational way.

For every living system one can isolate the sensing of external influences and the generation of information from these and the programs which are proper to this activity. We will dwell on each of these properties. The lower animal senses only certain forms of energy, in other words, their receptors are only of several kinds and these function only over a limited range of energy changes.

Information processing in the brain or in nerve ganglia enable the selection of a limited number of degrees of stimulus strength. "Recognition" of the stimulus is achieved by discrimination of nervous pathways which proceed from receptors by which the stimulus is sensed and by the generation of degrees of influence-strength by "superposition" on several references. Of course, only simple figures are recognized, figures which have models stored in the nervous system from birth.

Hierarchical models can be generated, but these are limited in number and in precision. Thus the qualities of the stimulus are defined; for example, speed of movement, magnitude, and so forth.

Conditioned reflexes, that is, the memory of temporary combinations of stimuli, are realized only by the conditioning of corresponding nerve cells — the thresholds of excitability and the frequency of impulses depending on the strength of the influence are altered as a result of frequent repetition of the same stimulus combination. It is also possible that some reserve nerve pathways are blazed, thereby creating conditional connections as in the cortex of the brain.

Noncortical animals can perform motor acts which are neither too complex nor too prolonged. Quite complex voluntary movements are ensured by the availability of the following components in the programs of activity.

1. Hierarchy of the models. The upper levels activate and deactivate lower-level models.

2. Every model on a higher level has several corresponding variants on a lower level. That variant is activated which is best prepared for "local" conditions.

3. Feedback signaling concerning the execution of the next stage of the program or of resistance to its execution. Feedback signals are necessary for activation of the next stage of the program, for its amplification, or for switching over to another program.

4. A control "servosystem" probably exists which checks the actual execution of the program against the "required" by feedback; that which is required being established from birth and only slightly altered by conditioning. In case of discrepancies, supplementary programs are activated.

5. A subprogram of "preparation" may exist. This refers to the activation of links under the condition of preparation previous to the execution of a complex motor act, links which are about to operate.

6. Supplementary programs of "amplification" activated upon servosignals identifying a discrepancy. Consider the special "emergency" programs of exceedingly brief amplification which

occur at the cost of nonproductive loss of energy reserve. We can conditionally designate these as programs of "emotions."

At the level of noncortical animals, special programs probably do not exist for the memorization of every executed program in order to correct the existing model. However, some traces remain which in all probability participate in the cellular models, that is, in conditioning.

We must dwell particularly on the "program of attention" — selection at any given moment of that one program which is most important for the organism. Such a mechanism must exist for motor programs, otherwise expedient movements would be impossible. They would continually be distorted by others simultaneously activated upon the influence of other stimuli. At the level of the spinal cord, such programs exist in the form of so-called reciprocal inhibition, when the execution of one reflex automatically deactivated others which operate in an opposing manner. There may be a program of domination in the cranial brain which suppresses all other models upon excitation of a single model (for example, an advanced model). Upon execution of the first program, the remainder are deinhibited and are prepared for activation.

It is probable that the program of sensed information processing realizes the amplification of some channels of reception at the expense of others. Those channels take charge which either experience the influence of stronger stimuli or which are particularly important for the existence of a system.

We can consider the noncortical animal as a complex automaton having a large collection of programs for the processing of sensed information and a collection of models of motor acts which are activated from the feeling sphere — forms which represent models of external and internal stimuli, these being previously encoded in the control systems of the organism. Higher-level programs, the previously designated instincts of self-preservation and continuation of the family, are the sole "engines" of its behavior. Models of these programs are stored in higher centers of the nervous system which collect information about the state of the internal sphere and, in particular, are subject to constant influence by the endocrine system. Exciting them, changes the "tuning" of the models-standards which serve for comparison with models of the external world or vary the thresholds of excitability of corresponding feeling centers. Thus, a selective, subjective information processing is realized and applied to the state of the organism at any given moment (hunger, reproduction cycle, and so forth).

The very same thing relates to the motor sphere: excitation of instincts leads to an increase in the excitability of some models of operations which ensures their domination over others which are less important at that moment.

Perhaps we should stop and consider the "feelings" of lower animals. The structures of nerve cells which realize the reception of external and internal influences, generation from the latter of information, and its processing into hierarchical models — all this is embraced by the concept of the "feeling sphere." Feelings are the excitation of some nerve centers (models), which receive influences from the body and from the external environment. For example, an enemy's odor elicits excitation of specific nerve structures in noncortical animals, this excitation moves to models of motor act-programs (such as flight). The feeling may be weak or strong, this being a function of the intensity of the stimulus and the tuning of the centers which, in turn is determined by the state of the organism. It is quite significant that models of "feelings" are stored in the process of formation of the animal before its birth; in general, the word "feeling" in its literal sense cannot be suitably applied to the majority of lower living entities.

Programs of operations, caused by an external stimulus and activated by "feelings," depend on the specificity and force of the stimulus. Sometimes these are light movements, limited by participation of only a few muscles, while in other codes, the excitation is distributed throughout the nervous system with the resultant mobilization of the entire potential of the organism within a very brief time span. Such a state of general excitation can very likely be called "emotional." With this, not only is there the activation of special motor acts, as, for example, defense movements or attacks, but also the regulation of the entire inner sphere for ensuring maximum potential muscle capability (an inner component of the program of "emotion"). "Emotions" are nothing more than emergency reserve programs, which are activated under excessive stimuli which threaten life, and this without consideration for the amount of loss. Most probably only negative "emotions" are inherent in lower animals — fear and anger, these being derivative programs of the instinct for self-preservation. Nevertheless, "feelings" are associated with reproduction, that is, an excitation of some centers-models which can be as strong if not as expressive as sexual reproduction in advanced animals. It is possible that the suppression of the program for reproduction (determined by feedback and "servomechanisms") is also elicited by the "emotions" of anger.

In general, "feelings" and "emotions" in lower animals are the excitation of feeling centers by stimuli whose range is limited by the innate possibilities of the organism. The intensity of excitation is determined by the strength of the stimulus and the tuning of the center by the internal influences of the body. This is analogous to processes of information processing in corresponding parts of an automaton, parts of which sense and analyze external influences prior to activating the mechanism of operations.

The group of cortical animals is perhaps even more richly supplied with an abundance of program variants than the previous group of animals. Of course, examination of the entire group from this viewpoint is admissable only with reservations. Nevertheless, there is a series of programs which is common to all species in this group.

The lower cortical animals are not clearly distinguished from higher representatives of the preceding group. The cerebral cortex of some is so small that its removal has almost no effect on their life functions. Programs of cortical animals, as those of any living system, can be subdivided into three types — "for one's self," "for the family," "for the species." Each has several variants, many levels and two subprograms — an internal one and an external one. It would appear that the scheme for the construction of programs is like that of the preceding group. The difference lies only in the quantity of levels, in the principles of information-processing, and in the specific weight of different programs. Thus, for example, in this group, there is a sharp increase in significance of the program "for the family": the instinct of reproduction is supplemented by the instinct of upbringing of the progeny. Programs for the family are represented by the behavior of herd animals, by the necessity for social exchange and not simply by the relation of instincts of reproduction and self-preservation of the individual.

As already noted, in accordance with the general laws of evolution, every newly generated species of living systems simultaneously carries old and new programs. Programs of the cerebral cortex which represent a new level of structures, ensuring far greater possibilities of information processing and in the creation of models of the programs of operations are superimposed on programs of the noncortical animals, thereby significantly altering, but not destroying them.

The basic purpose of the animal cortex is to process external and internal information with the generation of models at different levels, models in which changing relations of different external stimuli are remembered. The cortex is the modeling mechanism which creates models of the external world, of internal programs of the organism, and of relations between these. Its presence significantly increases the adaptability of the animal to the changing external conditions, and guarantees the best possibilities for survival of the individual and the family.

The diversity of the external world which can be perceived by noncortical animals is limited by the number of innate models. Of course, this number is not great and the conduct of an individual therefore frequently is of low utility. Representing in itself, a great cellular mass, the cortex permits not only increase of the number of such models but also imprinting in them change of the external world in time and in relation to the individual.   It is a self-learning system.

Basic programs of activity of the cerebral cortex, the generation of hierarchical information, models of activities, feeling sphere, attention — are identical in animals and in man as a whole. These will be described in detail, compared, and contrasted in the following chapter.

3

Basic Programs of Human Behavior

In this chapter I will try to state the general assumptions which underlie an hypothesis concerning programs of human behavior — concerning the mechanism of human thinking and the mind. Of course, these assumptions must also be viewed as hypothetical and, therefore, require serious discussion. I will attempt to confine myself to informational aspects, making only infrequent and superficial excursions into the physiology of the higher nervous function. (It seems to me that the time for a physiological hypothesis of thinking has not yet arrived.) We must first, however, examine some problems of human development. I will state these in the manner in which they are most meaningful for me.

Formation of man as a member of society. All species of life have developed and changed through those millions of years which constitute the earth's history. But no other single species has even remotely approached the human level. In terms of general features, from the physiological and anatomical points of view, it is not easy to find principal differences between man and the other higher mammals. But comparison in an informational way immediately makes it possible to define these differences. One difference lies in man's capacity to generate information from external influences with higher and more diverse codes-qualities. This permits man to see and understand that which is inaccessible to other animals even though they have well-developed sense organs. A second and possibly even more important distinction, is man's capacity to create models at new levels in the cerebral cortex and his skill in embodying these in things, using his beautifully developed motor apparatus.

Why has man been so elevated relative to his fellow creatures? We can point to two anatomical features for an explanation. In the first place, the human brain is significantly different from the brain of all other animals, including the other primates. This distinction lies not so much in the brains volume, that is, in the number of cells, but, primarily in the structure of the brains fields: the great surface area of the cortex because of its convolutions, and the development of frontal and temporal regions which do not have direct connections with receptors or effectors and which fulfill the role of a superstructure on the "old cortex." It is just these structures which ensure the generation of higher information codes.

In the second place, and apparently not as important, the direct control of skeletal muscles has been transferred from the subcortex in animals to the cortex in man. Extensions of pyramidal cells of the motor zone of the cortex reach directly to motor neurons of the spinal column in man. Since there are many more cells in the human cortex, the creation of more complex models of motor acts is correspondingly possible.

These anatomical peculiarities of man emerged as a result of a series of successful mutations which were "reinforced" by natural selection. There is little basis for thinking that transmission of acquired characteristics played any significant role in evolution: the chain of transmission of information from muscles which have hypertrophied as a result of exercise to molecules of DNA located in the genes of embryonic cells which determine the structure of these muscles in the offspring is too long.

In all probability anatomy has outdistanced function. We may assume that the human brain is almost the same now as it was long ago and that in the course of many thousands of years it was not utilized in full measure. Perhaps its possibilities have not yet been exhausted. (Other animals may have the same potential, as for example, the dolphin.)

The structure of the brain is only a prerequisite for the development of humanity. The point is that in the higher levels of the cortex inherent to man there are no models of programs which are ready for information processing. These exist only at lower levels—in the form of longitudinal connections. Information is directed along these from the subcortex and thus reflected into cortical analyzers. Transverse connections unused prior to birth, merely ensure the creation of temporary conditional connections between models of the external world, impressed onto the analyzers along prepared functional transverse connections. Thus, there is a network of innate channels through which information flows: gradually, in the process of acquisition of experience the "reticular" space between them is filled with only those models of the external world which are "inscribed" on the prepared network. Such a system (a modeling apparatus) may be said to be self-learning.

In all probability higher sections of the cortex are built differently. Here too, of course, we find longitudinal connections which connect with the "old cortex." But the conductivity of these innate connections is insufficient to account for the direct production of higher codes of information. Random connections prevail here: a multitude of surplus conductors form a complex nerve network along which excitation proceeding from "below" is initially diffusely distributed. Channels for the movement of information are formed in the process of repetitive exercise of the same line of connection—at first due to chance coincidence in time and then along paths left from the previous flows. Consequently, the structure of higher levels of the cortex is created and modified in the course of its conditioning. Going through a period of training, it acquires the capability to recreate itself depending on the problems given to it and on secondary external influences. Thus it is a self-organizing system.

However, conditioning, a preliminary stage of training, is a necessary prerequisite for activity of such a system. First, it is necessary to prepare, by means of repetition of identical combinations of stimuli, some "mainline" channels along which information will flow; then other "secondary" channels are organized around these and a network is thus created—a structure which predetermines programs of information processing with the generation of higher level codes.

It appears to be very important that, if possible, such preliminary training be carried out at an early age in the period of growth and maturation of the new cortex, which, as is known, takes several years. If this period is neglected, training will be achieved only with great difficulty and will, in general, not yield the desired results. Under ordinary conditions, this conclusion cannot be verified since even in the least cultured of families, the child will receive some minimal complex of lessons. Life has, however, supplied a natural experiment. There are known cases when four to eight year old children have been found in jungles, having been stolen and raised by wild beasts. Just like animals, they moved on all fours, could not speak, and preferred the community of four-legged animals. Significantly, it was exceedingly difficult to train them to develop elementary human habits. This could be done only within narrow limits. It took several years to train them to stand like humans and to teach them some 30 to 50 words.

Similar observations demonstrate that the "anatomical" cortex is merely the prerequisite for formation of man as we know him. Man is created through training, and society is necessary for this—as a higher system capable of accumulating information and transmitting it to its members.

We may assume that the path taken in the shaping of man was tortuous and long. Evidently, man's brain emerged a very long time ago, at a time when our remote ancestors did not yet have racial distinctions. These distinctions, such as skin color and skeletal peculiarities were generated later. It is difficult to imagine each race having its own great-ancestor or that an identical brain developed in all races which possessed different external features due to many independent mutations. Probably, the reverse is more accurate: first, the brain emerged, people then settled around the planet and only subsequently developed racial features. But, this is merely an hypothesis which remains to be proven.

Not only man's brain, but his external appearance as well are formed through training. I am not convinced that we walk on two legs because of our anatomical peculiarities. Let us recall with what difficulty a child learns to walk and how easily and with what satisfaction he moves on all fours. If he were not surrounded by bipedals and were not compelled to stand on his legs, he probably would remain on all fours. The proof of this lies in those very wards of the jungles. Of course, the vertical position imposes its stamp in the formation of the skeleton, on the internal organs, and even on the brain. However, the fact that primitive man quite frequently walked with the assistance of his hands does not demonstrate the inadequacy of his brain—rather, the brain was not utilized only because of a lack of training. Acceptance of an "abrupt" emergence of the brain does not preclude its subsequent "elaboration" by means of many small mutations. The same reasoning applies to the other parts of the body which have gradually acquired their present appearance. Natural selection played a great role in this process, with the gradual formation of "ideals" as a reflection of the criteria of survival. Man even owes his current ideal of beauty to the vertical position. Henceforth, if mutations were to generate long-legged and short-armed individuals, such individuals would subsequently influence the development of a corresponding racial type. The very same thing applies to the shape of the head and of course to the brain insofar as it determines the mind—a very important factor of selection in the embryonic primitive society where it was already necessary to invent, to remember, and to know how to make things.

And so, the brain developed and separated man from the surrounding animal world. A most important quality, which did not require training, was the powerful "reflex of imitation." This is the innate program of "computation," expression of a feeling model, and of image formation by motor means. Elements of creativity—the creation of particular models of movement—are inherent to many higher animals. But generally, these innovations are not imitated by other individuals and therefore die together with their "inventors." Man was more capable of imitation and thus the acquired, or more accurately, the invented movements were accumulated in the family. Primarily, this related to natural objects (to sticks and stones) used as too.s. Then, or even simultaneously, speech developed—a conditional code at a higher level. Some members of the family would develop a sound and, if it were convenient, others would imitate it.

Evidently, at times circumstances favored the formation and longevity of separate human families and tribes within which the accumulation and transmission of acquired movements and habits in the preparation and utilization of things were possible. Such families and tribes became the first nuclei of human society—of a new higher-level system which had its own programs for the processing and accumulation of information. Since they were separated by significant distances and because of travel difficulty their cultures developed differently, this in terms of the way of life, the tools, and particularly the language which is a most abstract system of signals-models. Certainly, most of such embryos of culture perished, since they did not attain a sufficiently high level of capability; some of them were halted in their development and have come down to us in the "wild state."

The basis of man's community progress lies in his accumulation of things and his improvement in the training of his children. The first stages of this process were the utilization of natural objects as tools for war, for labor, and the formation of speech—of a new higher level of code of signals which transmitted information economically. Thanks to speech the possibility appeared of preparing main channels in the higher sections of the cerebral cortex and thereby beginning its mastery—the formation of models of programs. Drawing was a new code which permitted preservation of information outside of the human memory. The birth of writing, still another code which replaced the sounds of human speech, heralded a rapid change in the process of accumulation of information and of training. Subsequent development proceeded rapidly: understanding of the external world, that is, modeling it by different codes; the creation of new models—of things, of tools, of machines. And all this took place during the course of an unceasing improvement of upbringing and training which ensured the mastery of the higher levels of the new cortex for every member of society. If the latter condition had not been fulfilled man would have remained an animal, only, possibly, more capable and more perceptive.

Characteristics of man as a system. Man represents a system which is capable of sensing external influences, of generating information from these, of processing the information with the formation of numerous hierarchical models, and of exerting influences on the surrounding environment according to multileveled programs. From a most general point of view, man is an automaton with programmed control. His programs are very complex. Some parts of these are stored from birth, others are acquired throughout life. These programs provide the potentiality for self-adjustment, for education, and for self-improvement. In other words, man is a self-learning and self-adjusting system. Of course, as is true of every modeling apparatus, the human brain has its limitations with respect to information processing, including limits of learning and self-adjustment. All changes of programs develop in time and depend on surrounding influences, both physical and informational.

I do not believe that we should be frightened of the word "automaton" when applied to man. The range of complexity of artificial automata is already immense and their history has only begun. On the other hand, this word emphasizes that man cannot suddenly deliver extraordinary solutions and operations which would not be determined by his innate potentialities and previous history of training and development; that the basis of activity in man lies in a program stored within man himself and not somewhere external to him, and that "freedom of the will," in contrast to determinism, is out of the question.

According to our general notions, every complex system has a multitude of programs which can be divided into two groups on the basis of certain characteristics. Thus, for example, as previously indicated, programs of every living creature, as a function of their point of application, of their effect in relation to the system itself, and on the surrounding world, may be grouped in the following way (Fig. 4):

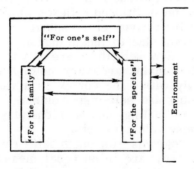

FIG. 4. Interrelation of programs "for one's self", "for the family", "for the species."

1. "For one's self"—which ensures the existence of a given individual.

2. "For the family"—reproduction and upbringing of the progeny.

3. "For the species"—ensures preservation and distribution of the species.

Programs of the first two types operate in animals, and programs of the third type are but their consequence. For man, however, programs of the third type are evidently the most important, since these have created humanity.

The limits of programs are arbitrary. It is, therefore, possible to distinguish still higher types; for example, those ensuring the existence of life on earth or something to that effect. However, if we approach this statistically, it becomes expedient to limit ourselves to the three enumerated above.

Although we have already considered the basic types of programs in the chapter on evolution, we should, nevertheless, dwell on them further so as to emphasize their specificity in man. The complex of programs "for one's self" is represented on a higher level in man by the instinct of self-preservation, which in turn can be divided into two components: "nutrition" and "defense." Each of these consists of a large number of particular programs—of reflexes of varied complexity with models of their programs stored at various levels of the organism. There are purely cellular programs for defense and nutrition, for example, absorption in the intestines or the rendering harmless of poisons by specialized cells. Of course, regulating systems participate even in these programs of defense, but only in terms of their own lower levels. The specific signals may not even reach the cerebral cortex.

On the other hand, programs such as the procuring of food, are located entirely in the sphere of competency of the cortex in man. Those signals which activate and regulate this program only enter "from below." This is also true of the general programs of defense. Here is a series of unconditioned reflexes which are executed unconsciously due to the activity of the spinal cord. There are even more complex reflexes due to innate models in the subcortex and in the cerebellum. However, these are only the lower levels, the "bricks" on which complex arbitrary motor acts are built. They are created entirely within the cortex as a result of the general programs of training and self-improvement. Still and all, subcortical programs of feelings and emotions play a specific role in the regulation of these voluntary acts.

On the whole, programs "for one's self" can be considered as "animal" because they are in an equal measure inherent to all animals. The difference between them, as they occur in different species, is merely a quantitative one. In realizing these programs-instincts, the cerebral cortex of man (as well as that of animals) fulfills the role of a computer, ensuring the selection of the best variant of defense, of attack, or for the procurement of food. The centers of such programs reside in its lower regulating systems of the body. Here mechanisms are stored (again programs) which maintain a constant internal environment and provide defense from harmful influences which may be capable of inflicting damage to the individual or even of destroying him.

Programs "for the family" can also be placed in the category of "animal," since they do not differ fundamentally from complex reflexes which ensure reproduction in the higher mammals. The basis of these programs is the instinct for perpetuation of the family. Its components are the sexual and parental instincts. The central link of the first is located in the sex glands from which emerge the basic stimulating influences in the form of hormones which act on the subcortex and also on the cortex. In a general way, it is possible to depict the entire program by the following schematic:

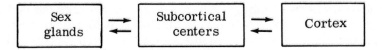

Man, as distinct from other animals, has cortical models which play a leading role in many of the links of the complex chain of motor acts which are united by the complex program relating to "reproduction." The subcortex yields only vague feelings—tendencies, worries, quests, desires, designs in the form of motor acts inculcated by training and creativity. The cortex stimulates, inhibits, and realizes instinct. It is possible that only such a fundamental process as pregnancy proceeds according to ancient autonomous models in which the cortex is only minimally involved.

The parental instinct, is very likely, more "human." Feelings to the child bear a biological character: their centers are located in the subcortex, and programs are activated from sight, odor, touch—in women, from the nipples while in feeding. The endocrine component is probably small, since instinct was developed comparatively late, that is, in the stage of the higher animals. This is especially true for the male sex. Nevertheless, the whole embodiment of instinct in the form of feeding, education, and the training of children is purely a cortical complex of acts, inculcated in parents by education and training. It is found in direct connection with programs of the third type.

Within each innate program there is no complete harmony of instinct. These programs were constructed gradually; to the old models of simple acts, new more complex ones were added, not destroying, but only suppressing the former. Therefore, along with synergism and subordination there also exist contradictions and noise. The cortex has merely intensified them. As examples: programs of defense activated by the influence of external stimuli are frequently in contradiction to programs of nutrition which are excited from within by hunger or thirst; cortical programs for evaluation of one's loves inhibit the blind sexual attraction dictated by the activity of hormones.

Programs "for the species" in man may be called social. Because of them, society exists as a higher-level system which exerts enormous influence on its elements—people.

These programs are found in the embryo of even higher herd animals, but at a much lower level. Social programs are not a manifestation of instinct, as we may conjecture is the case in insects which live as colonies such as bees and ants. These are the activities for the sake of the society, activities inculcated by upbringing through the cerebral cortex. The subcortex, with its feeling sphere, participates but secondarily in the realization of these programs. The cortex elicits feelings, these activate impulses, desires, and, further, again through the cortex, specific activities. The impression exists that man acts for himself, for satisfaction of some of his own feelings, but in reality he executes the tasks of the society which are inculcated in him by his upbringing. Here the cortex does not play the role of a computer which merely selects the optimal variant for realization of instincts, that is, of programs of the subcortex, but rather it acts as an independent structural unit capable of tieing in its own programs to the subcortex, to the body, and this regardless of the body's biological demands. Such "authority" over the body is a consequence not of innate power of man's cerebral cortex but of its conditioning in the process of upbringing and training. There is another distinction with respect to the cortex of various animals; man possesses the necessary anatomical prerequisite for self-improvement, that is, in man's cortex there are regions which are capable, thanks to the peculiarities of its own cellular programs, of receiving conditioning and increasing its activity significantly.

Inasmuch as all cortical programs are realized via the body, they always contain components of the lower regulatory systems with feedback to the cortex. These are feedbacks for every program and are also characteristic of the social programs.

The interaction of programs of the basic three types is realized according to the general principles which were indicated in the first chapter; independence, synergism, contradictions, and noise. Probably programs of all types operate simultaneously and without interruption. The point is that at any given moment some one of these programs is the main one, that is, dominates the others. However, this does not exclude the peaceful "coexistence" of different type programs at lower levels (for example, pregnancy continues while there is work for society, nutrition, and defense). As a rule, at any given moment, only one of the higher programs of muscular activity is realized. In the event of simultaneous realization of several such programs, only one will dominate, this being the main one. And this is understandable: a great number of muscle groups take part in a motor act and it is therefore difficult to imagine the possibility of a simultaneous execution of several activities with preservation of their general utility for the organism as a whole. There are, of course, exceptions when two movements are executed in parallel— movements in which completely different muscles participate. For example, a person may speak and at the same time engage in some other activity.

But there are other situations wherein one motor act will simultaneously serve two types of programs. Thus, execution of work has a social and an individual meaning, that is, the result serves society and at the same time it serves the individual and his family.

All programs of human activity have several features in common. Their principle quality is hierarchical. The whole organism with all of its cells and organs participates in any activity. Another matter is the degree, the relative weight of this participation. It may be negligibly small or quite significant. Contemporary cybernetics in its approach to the living organism deems it necessary to make a quantitative evaluation of the degree and character of participation of each component of the organism. Only in this way can we determine what can be ignored in the construction of models necessary for the control of behavior or for the treatment of disease.

The cellular level and the regulating systems. In this book I am not presenting a detailed characterization of lower levels of the organism—of its cells, organs, and regulating systems. Data regarding these are more necessary for medicine than for psychology and they were treated in the book "Regulation Of Living Functions and Cybernetics," (1964). We must, however, introduce some schematics since the significance of the "animal" functions is quite great even in purely psychological programs.

The general schematic of any program is as follows:

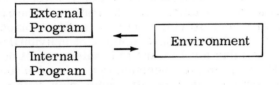

Man receives influences from the external environment via his sense organs and he in turn influences the surrounding world chiefly through his movements. This is his external activity. It is realized in accordance with the programs stored in the cortex and to a lesser degree, in the subcortex. However, these programs are not independent. External activity is always accompanied by internal activity—by the functioning of all other cells and internal organs. As noted above, in the majority of cases the internal programs are the principal ones: they activate and regulate external activity.

A comparatively detailed analysis of the structure of the organism in relation to its activity permits us to isolate several levels, although these have quite arbitrary boundaries: these being the cells, the organs, and the functional systems. Perhaps, it is more expedient to talk about the cellular level and the level of regulating systems, since the latter realize the coordination of activity of cells and organs without which the execution of specific programs is impossible.

All physiological acts can be represented in the form of programs. At the "lowest" level are the cellular programs which may be subdivided into three levels: the first is a lower level of working reactions, the second ensures adaptation, and the third controls reproduction (see Fig. 3). In a complex organism, all three levels have connections with its internal environment (but external to the cell) which delivers substances for exchange and activates working functions. In other words, the environment regulates the work of the second and third levels, that is, actively influences the capability of the cell with respect to adaptation and division. In the course of evolution, many cellular programs become specialized. This is true for cells of both the operating organs and the regulating systems. Other cells, for example, the connective and epithelial cells, have remained on a lower rung of development and form the basic part of the complex organism which has preserved its significant capability for reconstruction and adaptation. In differentiated cells, such as those of nerve and muscle, two phases of activity became sharply delimited: an active phase which executes special tasks for the organism and a passive phase which compensates for expenditures and which realizes non-specific cellular programs.

The study of cellular programs of a complex organism is quite important since all of the organism's activity is, in the final analysis, realized via cells. Representing a lower level of all programs, they carry a great volume of information. Unfortunately, it is impossible to model all cells; but this is not required even though one must assume that they have significant individual peculiarities. To model a cellular level means to create a model of an arbitrary cell in order to allow its inclusion in a general model of a higher level. Of course, this is attainable only within limits which approximate reality, particularly if we are speaking about modeling cells of the nervous system.

Study of the cellular level is quite a complex task, since, in general, it is not easy to reach the cell, and it is more difficult to obtain information from it without disturbing its life functions.

The nerve cell (the neuron), particularly of the cerebral cortex, is a typical representative of a highly specialized system. Its structure is designed to sense, store, and transmit information. Therefore, a cell has long processes—axons—for connection with the receptors, the effectors, and other nerve cells. Its physiology has been studied sufficiently in the last few years using microelectrode techniques, I will, therefore, limit myself to an informational description. Generally, this is a system with many inputs and one or, at most, several outputs. In it, the state of rest and the function of generating nervous impulses are sharply delimited. The impulse represents a complex physicochemical process which develops in time according to a specific operating program. It is distributed along the axons to the output. The impulse emerges as a reaction having positive feedbacks, hence its explosive character. It is developed under certain conditions in the body of the cell, and, in particular, at a specific place its potential must reach the level of 80 mV. The increase of potential is a consequence of the entry of impulses from other cells via synapses or as a result of some specific energy falling on the ends of the given cell, such as light or pressure. The cell may respond to a single stimulus with a more or less prolonged group of impulses of varying frequency. Most likely, with frequent stimuli, it will hypertrophy, in other words, its excitability will be raised. If the impulses enter the cell via only a single input, a particular synapse, local changes occur in it which increase its "conductivity" of energy. Some cells possess a contrary property to hypertrophy, that is, adaptation: the cell strives to support some optimal regime of its activity which emerges in response to the stimulus. If the latter exceeds some upper limit for the given cell, in terms of strength or frequency, then it initially reacts with frequent impulses and then, "having adjusted," responds in the more usual way. The programs of habituation in cells, expressed as a relation of quantitative characteristics, are most diverse.

Besides the indicated main property of the cell which consists of the capacity to generate impulses, that is, to be excited, a contrary state may occur, that of inhibition. Under this condition some active processes of exchange emerge in the body of the cell, and consequently it loses in varying degree its capacity to respond to stimuli with excitation. Evidently, inhibition is a physicochemical process which develops according to a specified program. This program is activated in full or in part from special synapses, upon their obtaining inhibiting stimuli from other also specialized cells, or upon specific combinations of frequencies of impulses which enter via the usual channels. In a second variant, the phenomenon has the name "interference" according to Vevedinsky.

In general, one can consider the nerve cell as a modeling system possessing the following properties.

1. The neuron generates information from the external influences, responding with its own code of impulses to stimuli which may occur in various forms of energy.

2. Different neurons have different programs for the generation of information; they react to strength, frequency, speed, acceleration or all possible combinations of these parameters of the stimuli. They can sum the stimuli in space and time.

3. The dependences between inputs and outputs of neurons are nonlinear. Certain values of the parameters of the influence cause the activity of the cell to fall to zero while others may transform it into a negative value—an inhibition.

4. The characteristics of a neuron depend on the nonspecific influences—the nutrition, oxygen supply, the physicochemical environment, and so forth. Various dependencies may exist.

5. The neuron is able to generate information of a second level, that is, it can slowly change its operating characteristics with change of regime of the arrival of external stimuli. This is expressed: a) by local change of that part of the cell contiguous to the synapse which reflects on its conductivity, that is, on its capacity to transmit energy; b) by general hypertrophy or by an increase of excitability; c) by an inverse process of adaptation—a lowering of excitability.

There are many types of neurons in the nervous system which are distinguished by any of the enumerated properties.

Work is currently in progress toward developing adequate models of the neuron. In principle, of course, we could create such a model but we must not expect that it would be simple. Besides, there is no universal neuron in nature; therefore, such work hardly makes sense in that it would be exceedingly difficult to create a neuron network out of so many heterogeneous and complex elements.

The control of cells is realized via regulating systems (RS). Gradually improving in the course of evolution, they reached a level of very complex multilevel organization in the higher animals.

A general simplified schematic RS is given in Fig. 5. Let us consider four such systems. I shall arbitrarily designate the first RS as chemical nonspecific, understanding by this the blood and lymph with their relatively simple chemical components— salts, glucose, amino acids, proteins, gases, "residues." This is the internal environment of the organism. The level of all enumerated substances is maintained due to the activity of many internal organs—kidneys, lever, lungs, heart, the digestive tract, and others. Of course, the activity of these organs is regulated by a higher RS, but many of these, in themselves, possess the capability of responding to a change of percentage composition of various ingredients with a change of function.

The second RS is endocrine. The principle activity of this system is that in responding to certain stimuli, its cells secrete active substances into the blood—hormones, which, operating in small doses, behave as activators or inhibitors of various cellular reactions.

Hormones differ in point of application and the effect of their influence on the cell. Some regulate working reactions of some special cells; for example, adrenalin elicits a contraction of the smooth musculature. Others influence all or only certain selected cells on a second level, directly changing their capacity for adaptation, but not regulating their operating function. Very likely, this is the influence of cortisone, a hormone of the adrenal cortex. Both relate only to cells of regulating systems. Controlling the activity of cells, endocrine glands are a necessary component of multistage structures having feedbacks. Moreover, they can prolong and intensify the activity of nerve regulators.

Several levels can be distinguished in the endocrine system. At the very bottom are found the "local" hormones, secreted as a by-product by working cells. They exert regulating activity within the limits of one or more neighboring organs. The stomach hormone, secretin, is an example. The level next to the bottom is represented by special glands which regulate the working function of certain specialized cells, as, for example, the carbohydrate

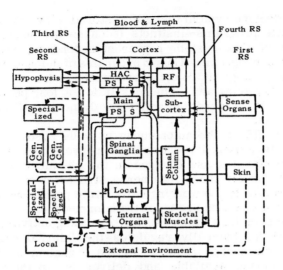

FIG. 5. Simplified schematic of regulating systems (RS) of the organism. The first RS represents the internal environment of the organism—blood and lymph —together with working internal organs which maintain their composition. The second is the endocrine composed of several levels: above—hypophysis, lower —specialized glands (sex), still lower—general cellular glands (for example, adrenal cortex, thyroid glands), still lower—general cellular glands (for example, adrenal cortex, thyroid glands), still lower —specialized, executing particular tasks (medullary substance of the adrenals, pancreas). At the lowest level—endocrine functions of certain organs, which have local significance. The third RS—is the autonomic nervous system. It is composed (from top to bottom) of: higher autonomic centers HAC with sympathetic S and parasympathetic PS sections, of main centers which control separate functions (for example, the respiratory center), of spinal ganglia, of local plexuses in organs. The fourth RS is the peripheral nervous system. RF is the reticular formation.

exchange in the liver. These glands are influenced by the third RS (the autonomic nervous system) and behave as servomotors, amplifying and prolonging the regulatory effect of nerve centers. At the very top is found the hypophysis—the "endocrine brain" which secretes a multitude of different hormones which act on endocrine glands which in turn respond by secreting hormones of a specialized or universal character. The hypophysis maintains the closest connections with higher levels of the autonomic nervous system. Working hormones influence it in the pattern of feedbacks. Somewhere in the middle of the endocrine ladder, special hormones of general activity are located which are activated at predetermined periods of the organism's life, as, for example, during pregnancy and so forth.

In the endocrine system there are stored very important links of certain life programs—instincts (such as the sexual instinct). Components of this system represent secondary, but important links for other programs. Thus in programs of defense and offense, adrenalin plays a great role, is elaborated under the influence of the nervous system, and influences it for a long period of time, creating a state of increased activity with mobilization of all possible resources.

The third RS is the autonomous nervous system. The basic principle of its activity is: chemistry - nerve - chemistry. Nerve endings (receptors) sense changes in the chemical mechanism in tissues, and convert these into nerve structures of various complexity and return to the working cells on the periphery in the form of nerve impulses which are again transformed into active chemical substances—mediators which exert a regulating activity.

The third RS basically regulates the internal organs which ensure that the energy required by the organism for its muscle operation is made available and delivers it to the appropriate muscles. The schematic, shown in Fig. 5, to some degree only, reflects the complexity of the multilevel structure. In reality, it is much more complex. Local nerve interlacings in the organs regulate the circulation of blood and the operating cellular programs. Simultaneously they send signals "upstairs" and also receive "orders" from there. Segmental and intersegmental interlacings combine the function of several organs and also serve as the transmission link for higher-level sections. At a still higher level "main centers" are located, in which are concentrated the regulation of several organs and functional systems which ensure any single function, for example, breathing or the circulation of blood. Over these are the higher autonomic centers (HAC). Integrated functions are concentrated in them which combine the energetics of the entire organism. Serving the needs of the organism, the HAC regulate the exchange of substances, heat transfer and heat production, water exchange, electrolytes, and nutrients. Under the influence of subcortical centers of the following RS and directly from the brain's cortex, the HAC not only reproduce "orders" for the lower levels of the autonomic nervous system, guided by information from "below," but at the same time broadly utilize the endocrine system which in turn is itself under the influence of the HAC.

A multilevel information processing goes on in the autonomic nervous system according to a rather rigid program. Every level has its own code of information in correspondence with its specificity. The higher the level, the more general the character of the information in relation to duration and the spread of the anatomical areas of regulation. With regard to the programs of activity proper: higher levels yield "general orders" for many organs and systems. "Below," these "orders" are concretized in conformity

with local conditions. Of course, programs of the autonomic nervous system can be somewhat altered depending on the state of the
organism and the external conditions. This is attained through the
utilization of reserve connections which exist from birth and of
programs of adaptation of the nerve cells which comprise the given
system.

The third RS is a structure in which important links of general
programs of instincts are stored—for defense, nutrition, reproduction. However, these links are more often subordinate than
controlling. They do not elicit activities, but rather ensure or
limit them, executing the role of feedback.

The fourth RS is represented by the so-called peripheral nervous system which collects information from the external environment and controls the outward directed activities of the organism.
These activities affect the surrounding environment through motor
acts executed by the skeletal musculature. This is the most rapidly
progressing system, the system in which the cerebral cortex
emerged. Compared to the previously enumerated systems it
possesses the greatest potential for information processing and
for compilation of programs of activities: the diversity of the external environment is infinitely great, much greater than the internal environment; therefore, for modeling it, an extremely complex
mechanism is required.

The structure of this system is governed by the general law of
many levels. Receptors of the skin and sense organs serve as
working elements for the sensing of influences and the generation
from these of primary information. Skeletal muscles, "assembled"
on the bony-joint skeleton, are the working resources of the influence. The spinal column represents the first level of processing
of obtained and imparted information. The upper (the head) end
articulates with the medulla oblongata and further—into the trunk.
Here is the first level for the important receptors of sight and
sound. On this level, programs of simple unconditioned reflexes
are stored, and at the same time it is a step for the information
processing of higher levels.

For the sake of simplicity I conditionally designate the next
level as subcortex. This level is set forth as the informational
plan of thinking. In reality this is a very complex structure
with many and varied functions. We can divide these into several
programs.

1. The level in which primary information about the external
world is integrated. Not only are simple conditions of the environment (it is warm, it is cold) recorded here, but there is an excitation
of innate complex models transmitted from distant ancestors which
are the signals concerning "enemies" (darkness, thunder, wild
beasts).

2. Feedback information of the state and position in space of
the whole motor apparatus—of the bones, joints, and muscles.

3. Sensations and feelings from stimuli of skin receptors, combined with sensations entering from internal organs (warmth, pain, thirst, a full bladder).

4. Models of innate motor programs—of complex reflexes for the support of equilibrium and coordination which function as the necessary "background" for voluntary movements. In animals the latter are also represented in the subcortex, but in man they are controlled by the cortex. A portion of the simple reflexes (such as scratching and defense) are possibly activated by the subcortex in man.

5. Programs of selection-domination: determination of sequence, activation of motor programs in conformity to the needs of a given moment. In man, this mechanism operates as an aspect of the cortex, representing programs of amplification, realized by the reticular formation (RF).

6. Programs of emotions which behave as emergency programs under exceptional circumstance. These include a feeling component (anger, grief, horror) and a motor component (mimicry, poses, and more complex acts).

7. Centers—models of instincts: defense, nutrition, sexual, parental. In man, only the feeling components have survived from these programs—love, jealousy, hunger. However, it is possible that the motor component is represented by those nonspecific excitations, those strivings, which we define as desires: to seize, to run, to seek.

8. Programs of higher reflexes—curiosity, imitation, goal, and self-expression. In man these are evidently located in the "old cortex," but, it is possible that they belong in part to the subcortex as well.

In general, the subcortex is the highest level of rigid innate programs. It is here that processing of external and internal information takes place and elementary programs of activities are concentrated, serving as the base for more complex cortical programs. The subcortex "commands" higher levels of the autonomic nervous system and thus the endocrine system as well. At the same time, all three lower regulating systems exert feedback on the subcortex—both inhibitory and stimulating in character. Complex innate programs of instincts are localized in the subcortex, but activate both the higher links to the third and the fourth regulating systems. In man, the cerebral cortex has a very special place in the fourth RS. It plays an independent role of guiding a huge number of programs.

Only the higher levels of programs are being considered in this book—their cortical component which is expressed in behavior, the psyche, and in thinking. Of course, the subcortex and other regulatory systems exert a constant influence on the cortex, but they have their own specificity which is studied by physiology.

Programs of the cerebral cortex. The cerebral cortex is the substrate of the psychic life of man. Models of the external and internal spheres and models-programs of a particular activity are concentrated within it regardless of its relation to any of the three basic types.

1. A system of constant innate connections.
2. A system of temporary acquired connections.
3. A system of "energy" (amplification, domination).

Let me expand on these concepts. A simplified schematic of the cortex is shown in Fig. 6. Information from the subcortex enters along the vertical connections, flowing into the many layers of the cortex (in the informational plan these are levels; in the anatomical plan these are not only layers, but fields, regions of the cortex as well). The higher the level, the less permeable the connection, that is, the greater its innate "resistance." At the very same time, the quantity of cells united by these connections, increases, as in an inverted cone. Cortical cells of various levels have different characteristics with respect to the codes they generate as a result of the information processing: they react to various parameters of the impinging stimulus with impulses of different frequency. The anatomical structure of connections and characteristics of the cells on the lower levels provides for the generation of hierarchical models of information according to the general laws of cybernetics considered in the first chapter. The activity of cells is expressed by their development of prolonged activity in response to a stimulus which arrives in the form of impulses from the subcortex. Evidently, the following dependency exists: the lower the layer of cells, the briefer their period of activity.

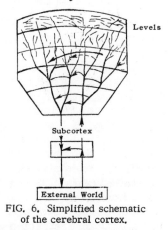

FIG. 6. Simplified schematic
of the cerebral cortex.

A system of innate permanent connections ensures "temporary" memory at different levels of the cortex (Fig. 7). In the example, it appears in this manner. Let us assume that from each receptor cell at the retina of the eye a nerve conductor goes to a lower level

of a cortical analyzer. Upon sensing a picture, part of the eyes
cells are excited, the remainder are not. The excitation is imprinted in the form of a corresponding mosaic in the cells of the
cortical analyzer and it is there that a particular image is created
of the picture as it appears at the given moment. Every cell of the
layer, having received a "push," generates impulses for a period
of time, let us say, on the order of five seconds. This means

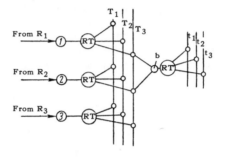

FIG. 7. Schematic of temporary memory.
Excitation arrives from receptor cells R,
R_1, R_2, R_3, to cells of the cerebral cortex 1,
2, 3.   Each is connected with a "relay of
time" RT — with cells which sequentially
switch over the flow of impulses to cells of
temporal layers of the first series T_1, T_2,
T_3. Excitation of several cells can be summed
in a cell of the second level b and can be
switched over from it through its own "relay
of time" to temporal layers of a second series
t_1, t_2, t_3, which "shine" much longer than the
first ones.

that the picture received at a given moment in the specified temporal layer will remain "illuminated" for five seconds. But let
us assume that changes occur in the picture every second. Consequently, on the lower level of the cortical analyzer there must
be at least five temporal layers of cells so that each second receptor of the network will be connected sequentially to each layer
across the "relay of time" by "shining" five seconds, the layers
guarantee temporary storage of the picture in the course of this
time period—in all its details. From the first level, connections,
well-worn from birth go to the next in which a higher code of information is generated, for example, certain cells realize spatial
summation. Several excited cells of the first level are represented
by one on the second level, but once excited will "shine" much
longer. Thus, a more prolonged storage is ensured—a somewhat
simplified, not as detailed, an abstracted picture. Consequently,
the system of innate connections allows the imprinting of pictures
of the external world sensed in a given moment and the preservation of the memory of those sensed in the recent past, this in the
form of a mosaic of excited cells. Various models are imprinted

on different levels in conformance to the innate connections and the characteristics of the cells. In general, all cells "shine" only at the moment of excitation or some time later. As soon as the stimuli cease acting on the receptors, all cortical cells become "extinguished": first at lower levels, later, at upper levels depending on the architecture of the connections and on the number of cells in each of these structures.

As noted previously, the higher the level, the less the innate conductivity of the vertical connections, the more difficult the excitation of their cells from an external stimulus influencing the receptor. Consequently, the degree of excitation (the "potential of energy") will decrease in an upwards direction. In order to preserve this excitation it is necessary to add acquired experience, that is, repetition to increase the innate conductivity of the previously used connections.

Most probably, innate connections take part both in the processing of information arriving at the cortical analyzers and in programs of the motor sphere. It is possible, that at lower levels there are innate programs for the simplest reflexes; however, this remains to be proven.

There is a system of transverse connections, associations (synapses) between the cells located in a single or in different temporal layers of the lower levels of the analyzer and also between different levels. These transverse connections are impenetrable at the time of birth. In the informational plan, synapses can be compared to resistance. Nerve impulses, passing along the conductor, carry some energy. Depending on the resistance of the synapse a greater or lesser part of this energy moves to the neighboring cell. This part is great in inborn longitudinal connections, but it gradually decreases in the direction of higher levels.

I will not dwell on the physiology of synapses: it is quite complex and as yet incompletely understood. However, what is clear is that the resistance of the synapse decreases if the receiving cell is excited at that moment when nerve impulses from the transmitting cell approach it. In other words: the resistance of the synapse decreases if cells along both its sides are excited. This occurs, for example, in the case, when both cells are excited independently along longitudinal connections from a receptor. From the following series of impulses, an already larger part of the energy will penetrate into the cell compared with the previous series; the potential of cells grows and if it were previously sufficiently high for other reasons (see below), it can be excited again. One way or another, the resistance of the synapse will decrease according to some nonlinear dependence on the frequency of its successful utilization. These temporary acquired connections are the substrate of "prolonged" memory. And so, the essence of temporary memory is in the active excitation of some complex of cells corresponding to the external picture. The essence of prolonged memory lies in the conductivity of the synapses, through which some group of cells is united among themselves. If some part of these cells is excited spontaneously or from without, then thanks to the low resistance of the synapses among them, the energy of excitation quickly passes to other cells of the complex (the model), their potential increases, and they all go into the state of excitation (they "begin to shine").

Experience is stored in this mechanism, which is realized because of a second level of cellular programs which perform local adaptation. When stimuli from the external environment continue to operate on and excite the same complex of cells in the cortical analyzer the transverse connections between them become penetrable and a model of the external picture, an image, is formed in the analyzer. This model can begin to "shine" even if only a part of the cells is excited as a result of the external influence.

"Self-organization" of the cortex is based on this phenomenon: repetition of random coincidence in the excitations of two connected cells increases the penetrability of their connection. Soon it is sufficient for one of the cells to receive an influence in that the excitation itself will move from that cell to the second one. It is precisely in this fashion that longitudinal connections are worn in the upper levels of the cortex connections, which were impenetrable at birth. Chance or preconceived (with purposeful training) simultaneous excitation of certain models creates penetrable connections. A further flow of impulses will select the more well-worn path and the connection is strengthened almost to the degree which could have existed from birth.

Thus, the mechanism for the creation of images-models is as follows: a picture of the external world is imprinted within a cortical analyzer via the longitudinal innate paths, this in the form of a mosaic of excited cells. If this is repeated many times, transverse connections are blazed between cells and the image is remembered on the first level. The conducting cells move the excitation to a second level, part of this crosses to new cells, paths are blazed, and a simplified model-equivalent is created on the second level which corresponds to the detailed picture of the first level.

Most probably, complete coincidence in time of excitation of both cells is not required. Let us assume some disturbance; suppose that one of the cells is actively excited and the excitation of a second cell is already dying away, the residual effect may still be sufficient for the synapse to be blazed.

Moreover, there are cells which behave as relays in time. They do not respond immediately to an exciting influence, but do so only with some fixed delay. This time lag is caused by inner cellular programs. Such relays are also activated in the chain of permanent memory created by experience; thanks to them, the memory can subsequently reproduce intervals of times which occurred in a sequence of external events and were remembered in the cortex. Clearly, these cells play an important role.

According to the principle of traces, so-called tracks are generated within the limits of cortical analyzers (Fig. 8). The point is that identical objects of the external world have different dimensions and consequently "fall" on different cells of the retina and the cortex as a function of the distance from which they are sensed. One cannot remember each of an infinite number of similar models. At a moment when we look at an approaching object, a gradual increase of its dimensions is reflected in the cortex: it apparently grows, moving from the center toward the periphery, but maintaining its likeness (the configuration remaining unaltered). As a result of the many repetitions in the cortex, paths or tracks are formed along which sensing of the change of dimensions of the figure occurs while it is approaching, moving away, or turning. If we remember an object as observed from a single distance, in a single position, and, subsequently, see it farther away or closer, the excitation follows along the tracks to more usual dimensions, thus it would fall on that very model-image which was formed by experience with the associated well-worn transverse connections.

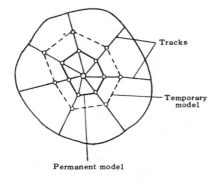

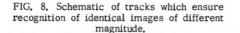

FIG. 8. Schematic of tracks which ensure recognition of identical images of different magnitude.

Acquired changes in synapses do not last forever. If there is no subsequent utilization of the connections formed between two cells, the resistance of the synapses will gradually increase, the connections will function more poorly, and with prolonged disuse the conductivity may almost disappear. Forgetting, an exceedingly important process, is based on this phenomenon. It permits those connections to be ready which are in the first row of memory and which reflect the most frequently encountered relations in the external or internal world during the most recent segment of time. These connections are also employed primarily in information processing. This is how rapidity of recognition is attained even with limited memory. Judging from the results of some psychological experiments, complete forgetting does not occur in that re-establishment of a previous connection is much easier than the original development of that connection.

Evidently, all models-images are made up of a great number of cells. The stability of connections between cells varies. Within the model-image there is a stable "framework"—a schematic within which certain features and details are superficially remembered. We can assume the same cells occur in many models because of the mass of conductors which interconnect them. Confusion in the reproduction of images does not occur only because these images are composed of a great number of cells. For a model to be excited, a certain minimum number of cells must be excited. Everything will then proceed in an avalanche-like manner, since positive feedbacks are activated: every cell in the model is connected with many others and influences these other cells when excited.

The energy system of the neuron is complex. A neuron can be considered to be a generator of neural impulses. This is its specific activity: it has programs corresponding to a type of explosive physicochemical reaction which is followed by a period of time before the reaction can be repeated (the refractory period). Evidently, during this period, some "materials" are readied which are then "used-up" during the impulse period. Activation of the impulse program initiates from some part of the nerve cell, in its body, or on an ending—and this takes place when a specific state arises in that region, that is, when some structure matures. Neurophysiologists have learned that one of the phenomena of this state is the magnitude of the potential of the cell in relation to its external environment. Such a state may emerge spontaneously and without noticeable external influences (though this does not mean that such influenced do not exist). Then, so-called spontaneous impulses are generated—a spontaneous activity of the cell. Usually, these impulses are infrequent. Specific stimuli or impulses from other cells accelerate the "maturation" of the state of preparedness and activate the impulsing of a given cell. Consequently, one can speak of the level of activity of a program for the generation of impulses—about the potential energy. The frequency of impulses—depends directly on this level. The activity is primarily a function of the particular systems of the cell. This determines the so-called threshold of excitability and separately the characteristic, that is, the dependency of the frequency of the impulses on the external influence. Activity (the potential energy) depends on the inner state of the cell—on its nonspecific processes of nutrition and on the degree of "conditionability" of specific structures which, taken together, determine the whole program of excitation. Resting on the general principles of cell biology, one can assume that with frequent stimulation and with good nonspecific exchange, this program will be amplified: the spontaneous activity will be raised and the dependency between the force (the energy) entering the input and the frequency of impulses at the output will remain in agreement. This is the activity of a second cellular level, which realizes adaptation.

And so, the activity (the potential energy), and, consequently, even the frequency of the pulsation of the cell depends on its state as an autonomous system and on the quantity of "useful" energy arriving from its environment. This latter quantity is determined by the total energy of impulses falling on the cell, this being in proportion to their frequency and to the resistance of the synapse (a measure of its previous use). Evidently, even the location of the synapse on the body of the cell has significance in that when it is close to the center the resistance of the inner-cellular part of the path is less. If that synapse is located at the end of a dendrite (the input process) the dendrite's own large resistance is added to the resistance of the synapse. Since for every cell there are as many as 100 synapses, the energy entering it, is determined by the sum of all these external influences (Fig. 9).

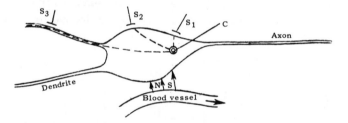

FIG. 9. Schematic of the nerve cell. S_1, S_2, S_3... are synapses with different resistance and different distance from the center C. A cell obtains nutritive substances NS across its membrane from blood vessels. Energy of excitation is derived from these substances. Energy, proceeding along the synapses has informational (signal) value only.

All associated connections of a cell influence one another; however, in the brain there is a special system which has the capability of particularly strongly altering the excitability of the cell. Physiologists relate this system to the reticular formation (RF) and centers connected with it. For the time being, we still cannot precisely say how it operates: are these usual neural impulses which are summed with all those arriving along other channels or is it a specific influence on some links of a particular program for the generation of impulses which performs an adjustment? It is known that these influences have a sign, that is, they can be excitatory or inhibitory. The nature of the inhibition has not as yet been clarified. Most investigators are inclined to think that there is a special inhibitory nerve network within which impulses also circulate but these have an inverse effect on the cell—decreasing their potential activity. Other investigators consider that the inhibitory structures are activated in the receiving cell—in zones of a kind which have an inhibitory effect when hit by the usual impulses. In other words, it is conjectured that inhibitory synapses exist. Finally, a third variant suggested is that of the "interference of frequency" of impulses. According to this view, with a specific frequency of impulses arriving at the cell, they, as it were, are out of synchrony with the rhythm of the generation of impulses and thus exert an inverse effect.

These problems lose some of their significance if we consider the cell in an informational way. Of much greater import are the statistical and dynamic characteristics, the dependencies of outputs on inputs with the cell in different states.

We now move directly to a description of the programs of the mind and of thinking.

Formation of cortical models. Thus, man can be compared to an automaton capable of multilevel information processing. A schematic (Fig. 10) depicts this in a most general form. The left half represents the perception of influences, the generation and processing of information, the right half represents the modeling of programs of activities which result in the production of information.

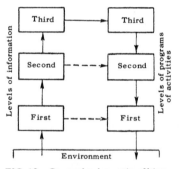

FIG. 10. General schematic of hierarchical information processing.

A general introduction to information, codes, models, and levels was given in the first chapter. We will now employ these as they apply to the brain. We have already mentioned that the content of the general program of hierarchies of information can be reduced to the following points: a) sensing and coding by neural impulses; b) creation of a temporary model—of a temporary memory of portions of the information; c) comparison of portions with standards—with models of symbols of a new code, thus performing a recoding of the information; d) its transfer to the next level where it is again stored, then recoded through comparison with new standards, and so forth.

We will dwell in greater detail on each of these points. Receptors sense physical energy and code this energy into neural impulses. In essence, this is already a first level of information processing: portions of energy initially produce some changes in the receptor; this is accumulated up to a definite limit, that is, up to the comparison with a standard, then an explosion takes place and a unit of the new code has been set off along the nerve-conductor, and the molecular structure returns to its prior state. Temporary memory concerning the sensed energy is deleted and the accumulation of a new memory is begun. The greater the energy delivered, the more rapidly it will accumulate to the limit and the more frequent will be the impulses. Units of a code of information are impulses. All information is transmitted by their frequency.

The nerve cell operates in the same way on higher levels, only here it does not sum quanta of light or heat energy, but rather some substances secreted across the synapse from the receipt of neural impulses.

Information coded in terms of neural impulses is transmitted from the receptors into the central nervous system. At the level of the subcortex it can be recoded in intermediate cells, "impulse for impulse" or with a decrease of frequency according to a specific nonlinear dependency. Receptors encode the physical influence which enters at individual points. To obtain a picture from such points, particular portions of the information must be combined, summed, and replaced by a new symbol or, more accurately, by those same impulses already generated by the special cell. The symbol of the entire picture is designated by the localization of the group of cells on some level of the cortex. All information processing consists of temporal and spatial summation of particular points and designation of the obtained sum by a new symbol of the code—by the excitation of a new group of cells (or even of a single cell). Thus, generation of hierarchical codes is reflected in the structure of the layers of the cortex, in the localization of cells, and not merely in the frequency of their impulses.

A receptor cell rapidly "forgets" the energy received: it is freed for reception of the energy which follows. In the cortical analyzer, on the other hand, the memory is certainly preserved for some time, this relating to how much energy the corresponding receptor had recoded in the first, second, third,... tenth second. This is necessary in order to generate information, that is, to mark not the momentary quantity of energy received, but its change in time.

Programs of temporary memory have already been described. We can represent these only in the form of temporal layers with reswitching of the input using a special temporal relay (Fig. 7). This switch initially connects the receptor cell to the cell of the cortex from the first temporal layer; giving the latter a push, the receptor excites it proportionately to its own frequency of impulses

at that given moment.   Then the receptor is switched off but the
cell of the cortex continues to generate impulses of the same frequency in the course of a complete cycle of reswitching—for,
say, ten seconds.   All this time it "remembers" the quantity of
energy received by the receptor cell in the first second.

The degree of excitation of the mosaic of cells in one temporal
layer exhibits, if we may so express ourselves, an instantaneous
picture of the external world, coded by the specific energy—let
us say, by light energy.   Excitation of a system of identical cells
in all temporal layers reflects a change of energy in time at the
point of the given receptor.   Change of the entire complex of cells,
shifted alternately from one layer to another, expresses the change
of the entire picture during these ten seconds.

The task of generation of information in a higher code consists
simultaneously of spatial or temporal summation or both.   We will
dwell initially on the first.   The matter can be reduced to the
identification of an image on a photograph; we must disregard its
change in time.

Such identification evidently occurs by way of superposition of
the mosaic of cells, which have been excited from receptors on
another system which is parallel with and identical to it—a
carrier of prolonged memory acquired as a result of past comparisons.   A schematic of the development of such a phenomenon
is shown in Fig. 11.   A second group of cells has connections with
an overlying level in which one or several cells are presented.
It is quite probable, that these longitudinal connections did not exist
at birth, rather that they were formed in a process of repeated
excitation.   Suppose that by chance it happened that excitation of
the unpaved (or for lower levels, the semipaved) paths from all
four cells coincided with spontaneous excitation of a cell at the
second level—thus making the connection somewhat more paved,
facilitating subsequent coincident excitation of a cell on the
second level.   Thus, in the case of the simultaneous excitation
of the four cells at the first level, a new standard has appeared,
this being one cell on the second level.   A second combination
of cells has its own standard, third—its own, and so forth.
As a result, that very same picture will be reflected on the second
level, but already in a somewhat "abstracted" form.   Thus, on the
second level, a new collection of cells is formed into a new mosaic
in which temporary memory is reflected.   Paired cells correspond
to them, combined in the model because of prolonged memory—
just as in the schematic of the first level.

Of course, we cannot imagine that recognition of a complex picture is realized using only two layers.   Undoubtedly
there are many more.   On each, a generation of some characteristic elements of the picture occurs, which is summed
on the following level, and so forth.   Somewhere "above,"
the whole picture or more accurately, only its unrepeatable

specificity will be characterized by a single small group of cells.

I have described only a hypothetical program of the hierarchical recognition of visual form. In reality it is far more complex since central and peripheral sight allows man to first consider a picture in terms of its parts and not the whole. I will not detail the named supplementary programs although with the utilization of other complex codes, this certainly becomes possible.

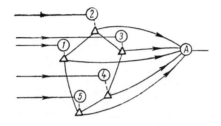

FIG. 11. Schematic of recognition by way of "superposition" of a model from excited cells of temporary memory (cells 1, 2, 3, 4, 5) on to a mosaic of cells of permanent memory, in which the permanent model is imprinted. Cell A is its equivalent on a higher level. Combination of these cells makes up a new, higher model.

The principle of summation in time consists of the following: Let us assume, that to one cell of a receptor there are ten corresponding identical cells in all temporal layers. Some of these cells are excited, others are not, as a function of the change of the primary influence in time. To each combination of these ten cells, there is a corresponding cell on the second level. Summing a specific combination from the first level, cells of the second level become excited and are no longer limited to ten seconds, as in our example, but instead are made to react for a significantly longer period, say, 100 seconds. As a result, a new combination of excited cells is created on the second level, cells which reflect in general detail temporary memory for 100 seconds. This combination of cells is recognized, that is, compared with standards of permanent memory by way of superposition, and information is transmitted to a third level.

As an example, we introduce a schematic which shows the generation of hierarchical models of speech (Fig. 12).

Of course, the rich range of sounds is at first separated by the frequency of oscillations in the inner ear; in the cortex separate cells register each frequency, sensing a change of strength of the sound in time from zero to maximum. Consequently, summation occurs upon the analysis of speech in the cortical analyzer, not only in time but also in space—from

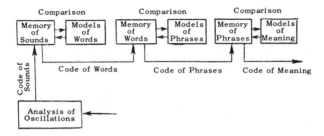

FIG. 12. Schematic of hierarchical modeling of speech in the brain. The ear codes sound as nerve impulses. They fall on the first level of the brain, are stored in the form of temporary models and are compared with permanent models of words. Then the information is transmitted by codes of words to the second level. There, it is accumulated in the form of a temporary model and is compared with permanent models of phrases. Subsequently, information is transmitted by a code of phrases to the third level. Again it is accumulated in the form of a temporary model consisting of symbols of a code of phrases, is compared with permanent models of meaning and is stored in the form of a meaning model. Programs of activities are activated from the latter.

cells, which "know" the different frequencies of the sensed oscillations.

For each cortical analyzer in the process of hierarchical information processing there is generated a system of main codes, for example, recognition according to spatial relations for the visual analyzer and temporal relations for sound. But, besides this, some so-called supplementary codes are employed, for example, a temporal code for the visual analyzer (its schematic is shown in Fig. 13).

The principle for the generation of supplementary codes is the same as that for the main one. Processes from cells of temporary memory on the first level go to cells of a second level (or of some

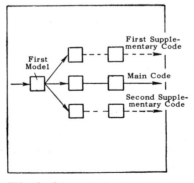

FIG. 13. Schematic for the generation of main and supplementary codes.

"supplemental" level) which sense other parameters of change of excitation. If we consider the reception of form as the main code of a visual analyzer, then illumination, color, speed and acceleration may be considered supplementary in the change of form in time—in the shift of the whole picture in space. In particular, cells of tracks may be employed upon sensing of supplementary codes. In general, the process of analysis of the external world occurs with resolution of its influences according to separate codes-qualities and by levels. Using receptors which sense specific energy, visual and sound information is generated from the picture. Its further division is realized in cortical analyzers: a main code is generated in the sound analyzer—a sequence of sounds in time; supplementary code—volume, speed, and timbre; in the visual analyzer there is form, light, color, displacement (speed and acceleration). Furthermore, every code can be reprocessed by levels, which select certain general features which are peculiar to the big picture—its subject, meaning, idea. With this, each quality is reflected in a corresponding cellular model which is excited in varying degree. The external world changes—a replacement occurs of its reflecting and analyzing cells, some are inhibited while others are excited.

However, in the cortex, synthetic work occurs in addition to analytical operations. I call this the formation of complex codes (Fig. 14). If we imagine the separate properties of the external environment reflected in different cells, we can easily admit that the reverse process also takes place: on some higher level a combination of two properties in the form of a summation in space or in time of excitation of two cells occurs in one. Evidently, this relates primarily to semantic higher-level codes. For example, there is the visual image of a dog: separately—lying, standing, running, or motionless, all this because of the visual analyzer. But perhaps the "dog is barking," or "dead" or is "ill"—this is now a synthetic image formed as a result of a combination in one cellular model of the qualities of sight, sound, and possibly, olfactory analyzers. Such synthetic concepts are also accessible to other higher animals, but only within certain limits. In man they are created because of the participation of speech (see below).

Complex codes of information are formed not only within the limits of a single cortical analyzer, but also between them—in the special so-called associative fields of the cortex.

First of all, several words about association in general. This term designates the connection between images which have limited similarity, frequently because of a secondary characteristic or, in general, through some third event. Associations can be of different types: a) on one level—between models within the limits of one analyzer; b) the same between images in two analyzers; c) connections through higher levels—through models of supplementary codes which are generalized over different objects (for example,

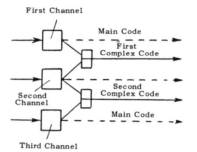

FIG. 14. Schematic for the generation of complex codes of information proceeding along several channels (for example, sound and sight channels).

through the image of speed or complexity); d) associations which are purely accidental—when two external, unrelated events accidentally coincide in time repeatedly.

The mechanism for the formation of associations is simple: if two cortical models have an anatomical connection, then upon their repeated simultaneous excitation, this connection is facilitated. Subsequently, excitation of one model will pass to the other.

In the cortex there are several different analyzers, one for each sense organ—an analyzer for sight, for hearing, for smell, for taste, for touch, and for pain. Moreover, there are separate analyzers for muscle-joint feeling and for the representation of internal organs. Analyzers are of a single type which offer potential for the generation of hierarchical supplementary and complex codes. However, each analyzer has its own specificity and different potential capability for information processing, this being a function of the quantity of cells and the structure of their interconnection. Besides this, the cortex of man has large associative fields, which provide for the "tuning" of the analyzers and serve in the selection of higher-meaning codes—of complex and supplementary codes (the higher the level—the more abstract).

As has already been mentioned, the higher sections of the cortex do not have (or at least, rarely have) connections paved from birth. Their utilization for information processing is made possible only after preliminary training subsequent to particular creative work. This is an example of the self-organization of a system in the process of activity. The essence of such a phenomenon rests upon there being a huge quantity of redundant and possibly random connections which, when paved begin to serve as channels for information processing—for the generation of its higher levels.

The mechanism of such paving can be illustrated by the schematic introduced in Fig. 15. An associative field C is arranged above the analyzers A and B. Let us assume that in each analyzer there is a higher layer of cells which is reached by connections

paved from birth.   Higher models are formed because of these
connections.   The connections which were not preset have great
resistance at the synapses.   These are directed to cells of the
associative fields.   Many connections from different parts of the
brain also come to these fields.   Upon simultaneous excitation in
the analyzer of models 1a,2a,3a,an association connection is formed
between them within the analyzer.   This yields complex images, but
not a new code.   However, conductors leave from all models to a
higher level—into the associative field,
C.   Possibly some of these intersect a
single cell, 1b.   So long as the paths are
paved, energy, entering even along all
three directions, is insufficient to elicit
excitation of this cell.   But if the cell at
this time will itself be excited on the
strength of spontaneous activity, the paths
may begin to be paved.   Evidently, a
single such coincidence is of little significance and it is doubtful whether a
second will be repeated within a short
time.   And the connection does not hold
for long, soon it is forgotten.   However,
a similar mechanism for the formation
of a "a higher representative" is still
possible—the probability exists for all
such random coincidences. The very same
thing may occur with analyzer B and from
this a higher model 2b is formed in the
associative field.   It is even possible that
paths to this model are paved from birth.
In this variant, upon coincidence in time
of excitation of models in the analyzers A
and B, their "representatives" are excited in the associative field C and some
connection is established between them.
From here, the paving of all connection—

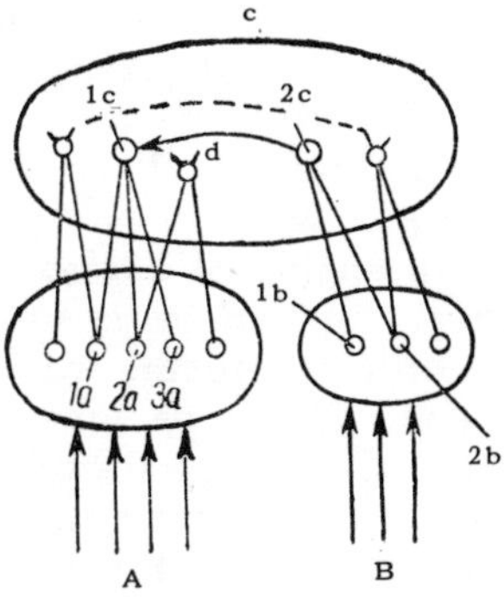

FIG. 15. Schematic illustrating
the formation of models at higher levels in associative fields.
Fields A and B are located in
the first layer, in the cortical
analyzers.   Field C is associative.   Cell 1c in field C corresponds to cells 1a, 2a, 3a in
field A. Cell 2c of field C is
equivalent to models 1b-2b in
field B. If 1b-2b are systematically excited from without in
order of training, combining
this with excitation of 1a, 2a,
3a, then connection d will be
paved and this will promote
the excitation of cell 1c.

within and from analyzers to the associative field—is facilitated
since cells 1b and 2b will now be excited from two sources, this
through their reciprocal connections.

    For man, developing outside of society, the described mechanism
is quite problematical, since it requires too many random coincidences.   But randomness is excluded as soon as special training
takes place.   Then the complexes of models in analyzers A and B
are excited due to the planned external influences which are per-
sistently repeated, and this at the same time.   Thanks to this, the
probability of coincidence of spontaneous excitations of cell 1b and
of the model in analyzer A is significantly increased (of course, the
same thing is true for analyzer B and for the paving of connections

between 1b and 2b). Pedagogy has established regimes of repetitions for optimum training in relation to the intervals between them, the quantity of material to be sensed, and so forth. The principle of self-organization is realized in that cells (or the models) 1b and 2b are selected randomly among many other possible variants, but if these cases are repeated, then connections are reinforced and they begin to function as though they were innate (or almost so). Training by planned influences from without is only the first stage. It provides the main paths within unassimilated associative fields in which significant disorder reigns. The process of learning continues independently due to innate creativity (see below).

Let us dwell on certain general regularities in information processing.

Intensity of excitation of a model. Every external stimulus is characterized by a set of parameters, some of these being quite specific in terms of energy—light, temperature, pressure, and sound. These parameters are distinguished by the specific receptors which sense the energy. Parameters of an informational character, such as change in time and space, combinations of these two, form, and movement are produced as the result of a multiplicity of sensing receptors which, as it were, quantize space and its changes. Change in time is determined by higher levels in the information processing. Consequently, all these parameters are "signed for" by separate cells and by cellular models—owing to the multiplicity of receptors, of temporal layers, and hierarchical levels. Combination of parameters is taken into account through the use of complex codes.

Intensity is the most important parameter of any stimulus. In certain cases its degree is delimited by the characteristic of the receptors which detect the stimulus when it exceeds a certain threshold. It is, however, more frequently reflected in the form of the intensity of nervous excitation, both of the receptors and of higher-level nerve cells. The parameter of intensity is expressed in terms of the frequency of impulses, consequently, by the amount (by the level) of the corresponding specific energy which moves along the connections. This is a very important index of activity of the nerve cell since the dissemination of information along conductors depends on it. In reality: if the connection is poorly paved and it has great resistance, then only an intensive signal will "pierce" the synapse and will transfer a quantity of energy sufficient to excite the next cell. A weak signal will not be able to do this. All this has direct relation to processes of recognition and information transfer from level to level and to the models of supplementary programs.

The probability of programs of comparison. Comparison of a temporary model of a portion of the information with a collection of permanent models—of standards in the symbols of a higher code—is a necessary stage in information processing with respect to the generation of higher-level or new codes. In the schematic shown in Fig. 11, it is arbitrarily accepted that temporary memory is reflected in the excitation of one group of cells, but the permanent memory is stored in another group which is parallel but otherwise identical to the first group of cells. Models in the second system are excited by way of superposition. This means that excitation is transmitted from models within the temporary memory along vertical conductors to a counterpart cell from which impulses are transmitted along transverse connections which, in turn, enter into other cells of the model. We can assume that vertical connections are permeable only "downwards," and horizontal connections, those between cells of the upper (the temporary) system, do not function. Furthermore, each model is comprised of a huge number of cells—thousands and possibly tens of thousands of units. It is therefore natural, that complete coincidence between cells does not occur upon the superposition of a temporary model on systems which contain many permanent models. Thus, the model in temporary memory, sensed at a given moment, differs from the corresponding permanent memory model which was formed on the basis of past experience. The comparison is, therefore, not identical but is rather probabilistic.

Consequently, for excitation of a permanent model the following are significant: a) the number (or percent) of cells which comprise it and which receive excitation from the temporary model; b) the arrangement of these cells—either on main structural lines of the model or on its "details"; c) the intensity of excitation of the temporary model; d) the degree to which the connections within the permanent model are paved. Actually, it is possible to recognize a well-formulated model even in the presence of a very weakly excited temporary model either by noting several "strategic" points or by recognition of an exact reproduction of a small detail. In the opposite situation, when the model is not yet "remembered," an exact coincidence of a large number of cells and their intense excitation is required.

Restoration of permanent memory. It was already mentioned that permanent memory is represented by the penetrable synapses which connect separate nerve cells. The degree of paving—the loss of resistance is a function of the frequency of utilization of the connection. Therefore, if the model is not utilized for a long period of time the connections deteriorate and the process of recognition is encumbered—an exact coincidence of a large percent of the cells of temporary and permanent models is then required. With change of a frequently sensed object, the permanent model is changed. There is a specific dependency of the resistance of the connection on the frequency of repetition. This also applies to the longitudinal connections which unite different levels. As they remain unused, they are gradually inhibited. In such a case, the required energy must be transmitted to the next level or there must be a great intensity of excitation of the permanent model.

The number of connections between models, arranged on different levels or in different fields, varies; this is particularly true in the case of the associative fields where the connections are formed in the process of self-organization. Naturally, the greater the number of connections the easier the excitation is transmitted from one model to another, and possibly the less the intensity of excitation required. In other words, the summed resistance of the connection between models is inversely proportional to the number of conductors.

The excitability of any neuron, which is determined by the amount of energy necessary to elicit a noticeable activity of the cell, is not invariant. It depends on the conditioning of the cell—on its previous history. Of course, this activity is directly lowered if the cell experiences inhibiting influences sent by a special system, or if inhibition develops in it, in response to the interfering rhythms from other conductors.

Thus far we have considered the "pure" case of information processing in which external influences are received by distant receptors. The energy of excitation is obtained from without and depends on the strength of the stimuli. Impulses are propagated along well-worn conductors and excite other cells depending on their cellular programs, in other words, on their preparedness with respect to the threshold of excitability that is associated with their conditioning. The real picture is much more complex, since the energy of excitation depends on many internal factors, and primarily on feelings, on the human reaction to external stimulation. This question will be examined below.

I have described hypothetical general laws for the formation of models, for the paving of new paths, the organization of new levels and the formation of new codes of information. All this is an essential basis for mind and thought. However, besides this, inner stimuli are necessary which activate all this "machinery." They are located in the sphere of feelings.

Programs of feelings. It has already been mentioned that the cortex reprocesses external and internal information. The latter is sensed from the internal sphere of the organism: from internal organs, muscles, and joints. It would be more correct to say that the cortex models both the external world and the internal world, that is, the body. Speaking more precisely, the cortex models the state of subcortical centers in which all information from the body accumulates and which process the information according to their own ancient rigid programs.

In the subcortex, many centers are concentrated which collect and process information from internal organs, from the muscle-joint system, and from the skin. All of these to some degree are represented in the cortex of the brain. An

illustrative (informational) schematic of the subcortex is offered
in Fig. 16.

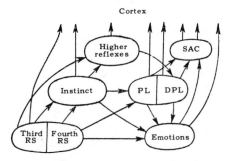

FIG. 16. Schematic of the subcortex (in an
informational sense). The third and fourth RS
are simple reflexes with regulating systems.
Higher reflexes are orientative, of freedom, of
imitation, and others.

First of all, higher autonomic centers (HAC) are represented
here, where general control programs of the internal organs are
stored ensuring the required composition of the internal environment best adapted to the needs of the organism, this as a function
of stress and circumstance. Note, this is not that homeostasis
which is generally understood to be an unalterable composition
under all conditions of the internal environment. It has significance
only for certain relatively stable components, the majority of
which depend on strain and emotions.

In the subcortex higher unconditioned reflexes are also located
for the maintenance of body position and for that tonic state necessary for the execution of any voluntary movement. For this the
subcortex contains appropriate information and models of movements—the higher centers of the third and fourth RS have their
own representations in the cortex of the brain.

Above this are arranged the apparent centers of instinct. I
employ the term "apparent" because they are not easily found—
in all probability, they are structures diffused over the subcortex
and which unite centers of the third and fourth RS. They exist
only in an informational sense and represent, first of all, models
of a higher level of instinct where information about the internal
sphere of the organism is collected, including both endocrine
influences, and, second, certain models of objects of the external
important for programs of defense, nutrition, and the continuation
of the species. In these centers of instinct general motor programs
are also stored which can determine both stimulation and desires.

Finally, programs of the already mentioned higher reflexes are
located—still higher, somewhere in the cortical boundary zone,
and possibly, directly in the "old cortex" programs of orientation,

goal, imitation, freedom, and self-expression. In these are developed their own peculiar supplementary codes from subcortical information. They control certain motor reactions or create stimulations.

Other important structures are depicted in the schematic. These are universal centers of "pleasure" (PL) and "displeasure" (DPL) in which the general state of man's being is integrated (these will be discussed below).

Centers of emotions—these are a concentration of special and emergency programs which are activated only under exceptional circumstances. They have their own motor reactions and exert specific regulatory influences.

Finally, the last structure—the centers of the system of energy amplification and inhibition (SAC) ensure the function of attention. Evidently they correspond to the reticular formation of the brain stem. The subcortical level of the feeling sphere is represented by all of these structures or centers. In them all of the basic feelings of man find reflection. Let us attempt to classify them.

Feeling—is excitation of specific subcortical centers, which is reflected in the cortex and sensed on the level of consciousness. In general, it determined the internal state of the man which is a consequence of the interaction of the external influences with internal programs. Possibly, it would be more convenient to use the term "feeling sphere" as a unifying concept. Then it is possible to introduce the following gradations which reflect not only the quantitative but also the qualitative aspect of this concept.

Sensations—these are, first of all, a weak degree of certain general feelings as, for example, hunger. Second, this term designates weak stimuli from certain sense organs—touch, taste, or the receptors of internal organs, (for example, a feeling of heaviness in the stomach).

Feelings proper—the usual degree of excitation of certain centers on various levels: a) of a local character on lower levels, for example, the feeling of pain in a particular area; b) excitation of certain higher autonomic centers—hunger, thirst; c) excitation of centers at a higher level, for example, of the center of the sex instinct which is the basis for love and jealousy; d) this also applies to complex cortical centers which cause behavior such as shame.

Emotions—the excitation of fully determined centers in the subcortex which have a clear biological designation (a more detailed discussion of these lies ahead).

Moods—a completely nonlocalized general state, a gradual expressed adjustment of the entire feeling sphere.

Sensations or feelings and emotions can directly translate from one to another. In other words, for certain states—these are direct degrees of excitation of a single center, as, for example, with the sensation of worry, the feeling of fear, the emotion of fright.   As applied to other states, one of these extreme concepts disappears. For example, for hunger there is sensation and feeling, but not emotion; for grief there is feeling and emotion, but not sensation.

Each of these three concepts can be subdivided into at least two degrees of manifestation—weak and strong;   however, these gradations are quite arbitrary and require quantitative expression.

Mood is a concept which is still less well-defined. We speak about a bad or good mood, about a sad or joyous mood, sometimes even with specification of the degree.

I cannot offer a detailed classification of all feelings. To accomplish this, even confining oneself to the informational aspects, it would first be necessary to assemble a complete atlas of programs. Therefore, I shall limit myself to a gross enumeration (I shall have to employ various designations for feeling and sensation).

The feeling of pain is a stimulation of pain receptors in different organs and in the skin which is manifest through the excitation of associated local centers in the subcortex. This feeling belongs to a number of lower levels which includes the sensations of skin temperature—warmth and cold.

Sensations from the body are fundamentally generated by the bony-joint and muscular systems. At any point in time man can imagine the arrangement of his own hands and the feeling produced by them. He senses obstacles and stresses as well as local fatigue. This is also a lower level: a simple reflection of the state of the receptors.   A major part of the internal organs do not have reflection in consciousness, but this does not mean that their receptors are not represented in the subcortex. Illness is accompanied by a whole range of feelings, beginning with awkwardness and so-called discomfort, all the way up to pain and special feelings, such as nausea. Asphyxiation belongs to such feelings (the feeling of an oxygen debt).   There are many other similar sensations and feelings.

Hunger and thirst are the excitation of specific centers apparently situated in the sphere of the higher autonomic centers of the third RS.

At a higher level, that is, in the instincts, more complex feelings are encountered. The source of these feelings is a reprocessing of primary information which enters from the body or from the external environment.   Frequently, these stimuli by themselves do not elicit feelings, but their combinations or temporal variations are reflected in centers of instincts. Thus, sex hormones activate the sexual instinct. In animals, certain odors, for example, those of their enemies, elicit operation of the defense instinct. And for man, certain odors remain unpleasant from birth.

I will not even begin to enumerate the entire range of feelings which can be elicited by the instincts. A special investigation would be necessary in this regard.   Let me designate only some of the more obvious ones.

The sex instinct elicits the feeling of love, of desire, of jealousy.

The parental instinct elicits love for the child, pity, sympathy. In this category we must also include the emotions of joy, of grief, and sometimes of anger.

The instinct of defense yields a sensation of hostility, feelings of hate and fear, and emotions of anger and horror.

The instinct of nutrition first of all excites the feelings of hunger, but, in addition, it can excite more complex feelings such as the pleasant specific sensation of possession. A similar sensation may be a derivative of the sex instinct. Greed is not only a quality but a feeling, it is also a manifestation of the instinct of nutrition.   The biological meaning of such a feeling is clear: a greedy animal strives to collect a surplus of food, that is, more than it can eat.   This is one of the factors which increases its potential in the struggle for existence.

There are pleasant sensations of endearment such as stroking and caressing sounds.   This is a consequence of the instinct for perpetuation of the species.   It is important in that it serves as a basis for vanity.

Unquestionably, the feeling of envy also comes from instinct. It is justified biologically since it is conducive to the struggle for food and for the female. Ambition, the love of power, has the very same character; even herd animals possess this characteristic.

As indicated above, besides the models of "particular" feelings, conditional centers of universal feelings of "pleasure" and "displeasure" are situated in the subcortex.   These have great significance since they serve as the instrument for the general evaluation of a situation, external and internal, which determines the general direction of activities, that is, to continue, to cease, to run or to strive towards something. It would be difficult to do this through each particular feeling simply by reason of the complexity of the structure.

An illustrative schematic of the relations of these centers to centers of particular feelings and to other formations of the subcortex is depicted in Fig. 17.

From one and the same center of some feeling, connections proceed both to PL and to DPL. One or the other of these is activated as a function of the intensity of excitation.   For example, that particular center of the temperature sensation which senses "it is

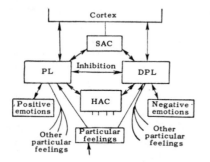

FIG. 17. Schematic of connections of universal centers of feelings.

warm," activates the PL; "it is hot" activates the DPL. Activation of one or the other connection is realized through a relay of the force of excitation, for example, in terms of the frequencies of impulses.

Both centers are united by connections which function as inhibitors. The more the PL is excited, the more the DPL is inhibited, and vice versa. Upon prolonged excitation of any center, adaption occurs and the excitability is lowered. That which was pleasant now becomes unnoticed. One can even draw certain hypothetical curves of the change of excitability or of the degree of excitation of each center as a function of the state of the opposite one (Fig. 18). Moreover, evidently an intermediate process occurs with excess increase of excitablity—a phenomenon of unique "facilitation" occurs after strong inhibition. It is generally known that upon sudden disappearance of some burdensome stimulus a feeling of joy develops, this despite the fact that no pleasant stimuli have been received.

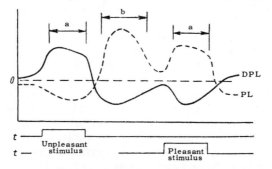

FIG. 18. Change of degree of excitation of "pleasure" and "displeasure" centers as a function of corresponding stimuli. a—adaptation, b—"facilitation" of the opposite center after removal of the stimulus, t is the time of stimulus activity.

As shown in Fig. 17, these centers have direct connections with the higher autonomic centers. It is also possible that there are inverse influences, both through mediators of the autonomic system (adrenalin, acetylcholine), and through the influence of hormone from the third RS.

These centers activate the emotions. Positive emotions stem from the PL, while negative emotions stem from the DPL. The PL and the DPL are directly connected with the reticular formation—in an informational sense with the system of amplification or inhibition (SAC). Evidently the cortex has direct descending influence on these centers, since they find reflection in the cortex. But this will be considered at a more appropriate point.

Emotions belong to the feeling sphere. Undoubtedly their primary "site" is in the subcortex.

By emotions we must include not only the extreme degrees of feelings, but also the special programs which activate specific sensations and complexes of operations in combination with an entire series of changes in the regulation of internal organs. In the biological sense, the emotions are activated when the organism finds itself in extreme conditions so that the general norms of regulation are no longer adequate. Here is a unique system of emergency operation which mobilizes all resources, permitting the greatest gain for a brief period of time even at an extremely uneconomical cost. It is true that such cost is primarily associated with negative emotions such as terror and rage.

In animals emotions are activated directly from the subcortex upon stimulation of specific innate models by the sensed environment, as, for example, by the odor of an enemy or of food, that is, as a result of instincts. In man this is far more complex. As a rule, emotions in man are activated from the cortex, as a result of any kind of conditional stimulus whose connections with unconditional stimuli were developed in the process of training. Frequently it is difficult to determine this relation.

A schematic of the connections between the center of emotions and other centers is shown in Fig. 19. Three paths for the activation of emotions are shown: from special stimuli through a center of instincts; from any feeling through the universal PL or DPL centers; and from the cortex. All these are inputs. The outputs are also realized in three directions: the tonicity of the second and third RS is raised and special programs of emergency regulation of internal organs are activated, that is, the whole system of homeostatic regulation (which endeavors to maintain constancy of the internal environment) is switched-over to new levels. Due to the activity of the amplifying system the "energetics" of the cortex and subcortex is modified and as a result the programs of information processing and of activities associated with the direct execution of necessary movements (such as for defense and attack) are sharply amplified. At the same time all remaining programs are suppressed. Finally, one can assume a direct activation or amplification of certain special motor acts which are inherent only to the specific emotion. It is true that in man these are activated through the cortex.

The number of distinct emotions is probably small since these are special programs associated with innate structures. I consider it possible to distinguish at most four emotions: joy; grief; terror; and rage. Note that only one of these is positive—joy. At the same time we can divide them into pairs according to the principle of contraposition: joy - grief, anger - terror. And now a few words about each.

Above all, joy is an extreme expression of a "pleasant" feeling. It comes upon elimination of very burdensome stimuli of of pain and stress. Furthermore, it can be activated by certain instincts, mainly those for the perpetuation of the species. This is a particular feeling of elevation in the process of "looking after" and raising of young ones. It occurs in animals and in an altered form,

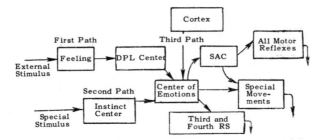

FIG. 19. Schematic of connections of the center of emotions
with other centers of the cortex and subcortex and of paths
for its excitation.

in man as well. Evidently, there are various nuances of emotion,
or at least, of its external expression. Specific motor programs
of joy in animals are expressed in mimicry, in poses, and by increased motor activity—running, jumping, and in some, by dancing.
Furthermore, in joy they utter different characteristic sounds. All
this is not only the involuntary expression of an internal state, but
also signals intended for the surrounding organisms, signals which
bear specific information. Changes in the autonomic sphere are expressed by a certain complex of changes in exchange, in hormone
content, and in sugar. Most likely one can find a specific "chemistry of joy," and another for each of the other emotions. Certainly,
these are distributed as electrical phenomena. The problem of
how to perform an objective diagnosis of emotions according to
chemical and electrical changes still waits for an investigator.

Grief is the emotion that is opposite in sign to joy. It is not
easy to say anything specific about it. I even find it difficult to
define its biological essence. Most likely, this is a particular re-
active state which arises upon loss of that which brought joy, upon
enforced disengagement of a program of instincts. Generally, grief
is associated with the loss of dear ones—and this applies equally
well to animals. This state is distinct from the simple excitation
of the center of "displeasure" only in terms of depth and duration.
Evidently, the reason is that the program for the love of dear ones
is in itself sufficiently long and stable so that its forced interruption leaves its own "vacuum" for a long time, drawing the
appropriate attention (see below). At the very same time other
reasons for the excitation of the DPL center are transitory. In
man the concept of loss is not limited to "biological" objects,
but is extended to work and to ideas as well. Grief is certainly
accompanied by great chemical changes since it frequently leads
to serious illness and even death.

Anger or fury—the specific emotion of offense—can be activated from the most varied of instincts and most frequently as a manifestation of defense in response to a wounding or other damage. In
animals the reason may be in the parental instinct or in the battle
for the female. In man there are "human" reasons, such as the

conditional stimuli of damage inflicted on the man himself or on his dear ones. The "outputs" of emotion are particularly potent: they can completely alter behavior and information processing (in the sense of evaluation and recognition of various codes-qualities). Thus, the motor sphere is reorganized: extreme stress on the energy supply ensures against the possibility of overwork and the signals from the muscles which point to fatigue are suppressed thus increasing strength and endurance. Of course, specific programs of frightening mimicry, and poses may also be activated.

In man, it appears that there are no special movements activated from the subcortex besides mimicry, but instead a program of "excitation" is activated which significantly changes the selection of concrete programs of movements realized by the cortex (we will discuss this below). Changes in the regulation of the internal sphere are very great and in particular are expressed by the secretion of great quantities of adrenalin which, in addition to increasing the energy developed by the muscles, operates as a positive feedback to the brain, amplifying or prolonging the emotion. In contemporary man, the emotion of anger is in the majority of cases "not vented" in movements; the motor reaction is limited to swearing or is in general suppressed. Therefore, changes in the internal environment are not employed in accordance with nature and frequently this leads to pathology. For example, the secreted adrenalin is not completely consumed in the process of muscular contraction and is thus detrimental to the coronary vessels. Nevertheless, willful suppression of emotions concerns not only the inhibition of their external manifestations, but also a reduction of the biochemical changes from the aspect of the lower regulating systems.

The emotion of fear or terror is opposite to that of anger. This emotion is activated by the instinct of self-preservation whenever an evaluation of the enemy indicates his superiority. In animals there is an entire series of external stimuli which can directly activate fear. In man only a part of these remain, as, for example, a powerful sudden sound (such as a shot or thunder). However, the significance of this reaction is not great. In man, fear is activated from the cortex through a mechanism of conditioned reflex. At the "output" of emotion—mimicry, poses, sounds, and excitations for flight, or their equivalent in man—there is a special adjustment in the selection of expressions in conversation. If flight is possible in the literal sense of the word, then the corresponding motor programs are sharply amplified, and all others are suppressed. Influences on the internal sphere, evidently are the very same as with the emotion of anger, but certainly there are differences. A specific biochemistry of fear must exist.

Human emotions are further distinguished in that they are remembered for a long time. The cortex with its memory serves in the role of positive feedback along with the endocrine system.

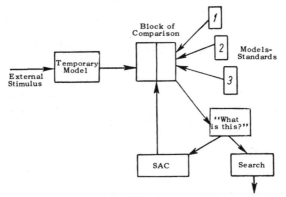

FIG. 20. Schematic of the orientation reflex. A temporary
model is in temporary memory. Models-standards are models
of standards from permanent memory. Search is motor models
for obtaining information. "What is this" is a special feeling.

One can conditionally relate complex reflexes to the feelings
sphere as has been mentioned more than once. It is possible that
these models are localized in the oldest sections of the cortex and
not in the subcortex. The essence of complex reflexes lies in their
particular programs which do not operate independently but rather
are superimposed on other motor programs, even to their control,
this according to the hierarchical principle (see below). However,
these reflexes have direct relation to the feelings sphere since
activation of the motor programs is accompanied by specific feelings which are then realized in operations or other excitations.

The orientation reflex—"what is this?"—is activated in the
event that an operating stimulus is not recognized immediately after
it is sensed, this because of the absence of relevant models in permanent memory or the fact that they are suppressed to the extent
that its own energy is insufficient for penetration of the inhibited
connections. A simple schematic for this reflex is shown in Fig.
20. If a suitable model is not to be found within a certain time
span, a feeling of "curiosity" will be activated with the question
"what is this?" A connection proceeds from it to the system of
amplification which increases the power of the first model and to
models of the programs of "search" which represent activity
directed toward obtaining supplementary information about the object. Depending on the code of information other questions may be
raised: "Where?" "Why?" and so forth. In a specific case, this
feeling can have different shades of surprise, of bewilderment, of
doubt.

The next reflex is imitation. Its essence in man: the sight of
certain activity executed by others, generates a desire to copy
them. This reflex is also innate to animals, but to a lesser degree.
Its nature, evidently consists in automatic "computation" of information—in the translation of a visual or sound image into a
model of the motor act. Upon the reflex of imitation, as it were,

a motor program of the general property which we call "desire" is directly activated.

The reflex of goal is a striving to complete an activity which has been started. If it is interrupted for some external reason a feeling of dissatisfaction is generated for which it is difficult to find an exact name. The reflex of goal activates supplementary programs of amplification by means of which obstacles are overcome and an attempt is made to finish the activity. The reflex is evidently activated from the universal servosystem which "observes" all programs. The normal execution, and particularly the completion of programs is accompanied by a pleasant feeling. Its expectation is the reflex of goal.

The reflex of freedom is associated in character with the preceding reflex: restriction of activities by external circumstance elicits a feeling of protest which activates programs for overcoming the restrictions, even to the utilization of the emotion of anger. The protest can be even stronger than the need for it. The reflex is activated by a servosystem and the mechanism which provides foresight of the results of the activities.

Possibly, it is well to isolate still another reflex, that of self-expression. The striving to express one's experiences and feelings is innate to all animals. The expressions take the form of poses, mimicry, and sounds. In man these sounds take the form of intelligible phrases.

There is still another supplementary feeling or sensation—time. Even in animals there is a "service of time"—a combination of certain cells execute the role of a clock or a measure of time. They are an indispensable component of all programs—both for modeling of the external environment and in the conduct of particular activities. The models created by the brain must reflect not only the sequencing of activities but also the scale of time. Disturbance of this scale is a source of a whole series of different feelings and sensations expressed by words: expectation; surprise; unexpectedness; bewilderment; disappointment; the specific one depending upon the programs in which the time participates.

All elementary feelings are generated in the subcortex or in the lowest regions of the cortex. They represent the excitation of specific cellular structures, elicited by the change of the internal state of the organism or by external influences on it. In noncortical animals, this activates corresponding simple or complex motor programs; the "feelings" themselves are not realized.

In cortical animals, the situation has somewhat changed. On the one hand, direct activation of all activities in the subcortex has been preserved. On the other, the cortex has begun to interfere, stimulating or restraining motor programs in those cases where conditional stimuli were in past experience associated with strong unconditional stimuli which acted on "feelings." Evidently, the cortex of animals does not directly influence the motor link of a program. It can regulate activities only through the subcortical center of "feelings."

To admit the possibility of such a program it is essential to make certain assumptions. First of all, the cortex must model subcortical centers of "feelings" in the same way as it models external influences sensed by receptors and which most often also pass through the subcortex. Then it is necessary to assume descending influences from the cortex to subcortical centers of "feelings." This permits us to conjecture that the cortex establishes temporary dependencies between external conditional indifferent stimuli which by themselves do not elicit "feelings" and those important stimuli which do elicit "feelings." After such connections (taking time into account) have been established, the conditional stimulus elicits excitation of the cortical center of "feelings," it descends "below," stimulates the subcortical "rational" center and by means of this activates or inhibits the program of activities. Here is the substance of the conditioned reflex. It operates with the obligatory participation of "feelings." Furthermore, the cortex remembers each executed conditioned reflex and correspondingly corrects those that follow.

In man the situation is made even more complex since part of his motor programs are activated directly in the cortex. Furthermore, in comparison with his evolutionary predecessors his capability with respect to information processing, both internal and external, has grown strongly. Nevertheless, the principle of the cortical modeling of feelings has remained in him. Let us attempt to understand this situation.

The cortex models the internal sphere in the same way as it does the external environment. This means that all subcortical centers of feelings have "representatives" in the cortex, this in the form of models-images with well-worn innate connections from "below to above." Consequently, the excitability of the cortical models is high. Besides the ascending paths there are descending paths: when the cortical center of feelings is excited from a model of some irrelevant external stimulus, excitation "descends" below into the subcortex and is transmitted to the subcortical center of feelings, even if it is not excited from the receptors of the body. Most likely, the penetrability of the descending path is significantly less than that of the ascending path—surely in the majority of cases the subcortex attaches feelings to consciousness, that is, to the cortex, but not vice versa. However, it is in just this that the cortex of man is peculiar, that under the influence of society and as a result of one's own creativity, its models can be significantly amplified and dictate its "own will" to the subcortex.

And so, in the cortex, associative connections are formed between models of external and internal stimuli—of feelings. In making these connections time-dependent relays can be included. Their penetrability changes in accordance with the general laws of permanent memory.

Various hierarchical codes may be developed in the cortex from the feelings themselves, these indicating their intensity and duration. Many complex codes are developed from a combination of different simple feelings according to the general principles of the generation of codes and associations. The very same thing applies to the combination of images of external stimuli with models of feelings, both simple and complex. An appropriate schematic is shown in Fig. 21.

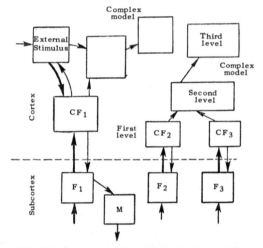

FIG. 21. Schematic of models of feelings. CF_1, CF_2, CF_3, are cortical models of "primary" feelings. F_1, F_2, F_3 are subcortical centers of feelings. M is the subcortical motor center.

Formation of complex codes—of complex feelings occurs according to the general principles of training and self-organization. Since there are many primary feelings and still more gradations of these in terms of strength, an immense number of combinations is possible, particularly if we include temporal relations. It is, however, doubtful that stable models of complex feelings of different gradations exist: surely higher levels are organized because of random coincidences. And here speech offers aid. Words designate different combinations of primary feelings and serve as the most important medium for determination of their centers in the higher levels of the cortex during the process of self-organization. Any person can notice how difficult it is to define feelings, that is, to delimit them. Perhaps each of us has his own individual criteria for recognition of the higher concepts, such as, justice, condescension, and so forth. Without speech, that is, without the words which "organize" concepts, man would only have access to the most elementary feelings which are directly modeled from the subcortex—hunger, fear, and some others.

Thanks to the rich connections between models of the external world and feelings, it is possible to speak about "feeling coloration" of many as it were abstract concepts expressed by words or by concrete sight and sound images. For example, we always associate the work "kitten" with something warm, tender, and pleasant. This is a universal phenomenon. "Impersonals" in the feeling relation of words are very likely in the minority.

To decode the origin of complex feelings, that is, to find their sources in simple feelings, requires special complex work. It is, however, essential to consider that the source of many of these feelings, or at least of their components are social concepts, and not biological feelings.

Feelings are a source of energy for cortical models. Exciting and inhibiting influences on the cortex come from the subcortex. Models of feelings occupy an important place in this process. This is understandable: feelings stand on guard for the well-being of the individual; they are an expression of his programs "for one's self" and "for the family." The high level of energy of the sub-cortex is evidently determined by the constant stimulation of its cells from "below"—from the body and possibly is explained simply by their specificity, that is, by the parameters of their cellular programs.

To a first approximation feelings reflect the "animal" programs in the cortex—the instincts and reflexes. However, they have a direct relation also to the programs for hierarchical information processing and the generation of higher-level codes and codes-qualities. They impart "subjectivity" to this process. Let me make this more explicit.

An indispensable stage in the selection of information is the comparison of portions of information drawn from temporary memory, transcribed in terms of symbols of a lower code, with models-standards expressed in the symbols of a higher code. As mentioned previously, this comparison is probabilistic and not simply a search for identity. As a result of this comparison, the required model in symbols of a higher code will come into a state of excitation and in this way there occurs a recognition of a portion of the information drawn from temporary memory. The primary excitability of a model-standard is important: the higher this is, the fewer the number of points essential for coincidence. A single model drawn from the temporary memory can be "similar" to several variants of the models-standards according to some of its characteristic and yet completely different in relation to all of the remaining qualities. Since each model-standard has some connections with feelings, its excitability is found as a function of their energy, this being determined by the internal state of the organism or some attendant factors. In the comparison, first, the most excited model-standard is "served" and upon the condition that it is

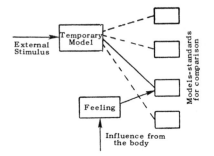

FIG. 22. Schematic illustrating the subjectivity
of recognition.

suitable at least to some degree of probability, it is selected, even though it may not be the most "correct" (Fig. 22).

Programs of activities. Man is an automaton which senses, processes, and imparts information to the external environment. The previous sections treated only the sensing and processing. Now we will consider the transfer of information and of activity. Undoubtedly, these are no less important and perhaps more difficult programs since they necessarily embrace information processing connected with the execution of a motor act.

It is known that an "automaton" is comprised of operating and controlling systems. This classification is also applicable to an organism: muscles are the working systems in it, fastened to bones and joints, and the nervous system is the controlling system. However, in reality, things are much more complex. The working organs—the muscles—in turn represent very complex systems having their own working reactions and control levels. These impart the capacity to change in the course of the activity. The concept of "control organ" is in principle completely applicable to the nervous system; however, it is necessary to consider that it itself receives influences not only from without, but also from within—from other regulating systems.

The primary difference between an organism and a technological control system is in the multilevel control of movements. This leads to complication of the living system that is so great that there is nothing as yet in technology similar to it.

An organism acts—that is, transmits information to the surrounding objects according to a determined program. This program is activated by influences from without—from the external stimuli. In this regard the internal sphere serves as an error—correcting system. The reverse phenomenon may occur when the program is activated from "within." Then the roles change: the external situation fulfills the error-correcting role.

We will consider the first case. Suppose that programs of activity have already been formulated earlier in the process of training and due to the person's own creativity (see below). This means that to each model of the external world (models of its influences), there corresponds a specific program of activity. The schematic is simple:

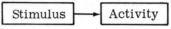

However, reality is much more complex. First of all, to the majority of stimuli, there corresponds not just a single program, but rather many programs which are distinguished not only quantitatively in terms of the tempo and intensity of their execution, but qualitatively as well—by the character of the response reaction. In response to insult, man can give expression to his feelings or suppress them. For this and other activities, there are preset programs in the brain; thus it is worthwhile to raise the question concerning the selection of programs. This selection is realized after an analysis of the external circumstance; that is, after an evaluation of the possible consequences of this or that variant of activity. Thus, a short-term or prolonged effort toward the selection of an optimal variant precedes the beginning of activity. This occurs both in man and in lower animals, most frequently without the participation of consciousness. The schematic for such a program of preliminary evaluation and selection is shown in Fig. 23.

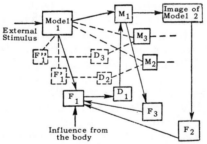

FIG. 23. Schematic of the participation of the feeling sphere in the selection of a program of activities. Model 1 is a temporary model of the external stimulus. The image of model 2 is the image of the future stimulus after completion of the activity. F_1, $F_{1'}$, $F_{1''}$ are variants of feelings associated with the external stimulus; D_1, D_2, D_3 are corresponding variants of desires; M_1, M_2, M_3 are variants of motor programs; F_3 are feelings associated with the execution of activities; F_2 are feelings which are anticipated after completion of the activity. Their signs may or may not coincide with the primary feeling F_1.

The external stimulus is imprinted in temporary memory and is recognized by already known programs. That is to say, suppose that some model 1 in permanent memory is excited. Many cortical models of feelings are connected with it—F_1, F_1', F_1'' Each is influenced from "below"—from the body. As a result of comparison of their excitability (their preparedness), the feeling F_1 is excited. From it, the excitation moves to the subcortical model of feeling. One feeling is excited to a considerable extent, others to a much lesser degree (incidentally it is possible to dispense with this supposition). For every simple feeling in the subcortex, there corresponds some elementary activity which we shall call "desire" or "excitation." These are ancient simple programs similar to the unconditioned reflex but on a higher level. Elementary desires can be expressed with simple words (with excitations), such as "run," "hit," "seize," "throw," and possibly even more general ones: the positive reaction being a striving to master something, while the negative reaction is to depart, to leave.

For every feeling, there are corresponding specific desires (in our example, for the strongest feeling F_1, there is the desire D_1).

To a model of an external stimulus there corresponds several possible variants of activities D_3, D_1, D_2. Each of these has its own meaning in terms of the previous experience. This determines the stability of paving of the connections to D_1, D_2, D_3. However, the selection of an optimal activity depends not only on this but also on the reflection of each of the variants in the organism, in other words, on the feelings elicited by the realization of one or another activity. Here complex computations occur although they occupy at most only an instant of time.

First of all, the selection of activity is determined by desire—this gives it direction: to fight or to flee. Therefore, some of the variants immediately become superfluous. A selection is made among those that remain according to the degree of exhaustion—of paving of connections with the model of the external stimulus. With each form of activity D_1, D_2, and D_3 (selection has already been made of those which correspond to the given desire D) specific feelings are associated and thus arise in the process of its execution. These are reinforced in the memory by past experience. As a result, F_3, F_3', and F_3'' are excited which characterize possible difficulties which might be encountered upon execution of the programs. Furthermore, for each activity D there is a corresponding image of its consequences: that is, a reflection of the stimulus execution by the given activity. This is also related to the feeling F_2, which in general corresponds to desire—not highly specific in detail but clear in terms of the direction of activity.

And so, as a result there are collections of feelings, F_1, F_2, F_3; each having several variants (F_2', F_2'', F_2). The selection of optimum activity is done by comparison of these feelings according to sign and intensity. Although feelings can be highly "particular" (for example, the sensation of pain and of hunger), they are comparable since each such feeling has connection with the centers of "pleasure" and "displeasure." It is in these centers that the comparison occurs. The result is a selection and amplification of a single F_1 —of the primary feeling elicited by the external stimulus. It may turn out that the first excitation will be rejected and another feeling will replace it. At the moment when variant F_1 has been defined, it is simultaneously amplified to some degree. The "energy" of F_1 depends on this degree, in other words, this corresponds to the degree of desire: "I want very strongly" or "I barely want." After the desire has been precisely determined, there is no real difficulty in the selection of one of the number of several variants of activity corresponding to it. This is done by comparing the feelings F_3, F_3', and F_3'', associated with the execution of future work: the complexity of each variant is evaluated as is the possible encumberances linked with each of them.

With this the first phase is completed: there has been a selection of an optimal program of activities. I repeat, to a large measure, this process depends on the state of the organism at the given moment, that is, it tends to be quite subjective.

The activity itself follows.

All programs of activities are multileveled. This means that at the very top there is a model of the idea of a motor act, at a lower level there are models of the sequence of particular separate movements, still lower there is the order for the contraction of muscles within each movement. This ladder can extend even further: to the distribution of contractile and noncontractile fibrils in the muscle itself, the biochemical processes occurring in the muscle fibril, and so forth. Human activities can be very complex and prolonged. The number of higher levels significantly increases for people who select a program of activity for many years in advance.

The hierarchical construction of programs is extremely profitable in that the required volume of memory is reduced. If programs were "stretched in one line," as occurs in electronic computers, then for each of them it would be necessary to remember the whole sequence of elementary activities. With hierarchical construction all programs consist of standard elementary movements, collection of which is performed on a lower level. Only the order of their activation is remembered on the upper levels. One can make standard "blocks" from elementary ones and, designating these by codes build a third level—a collection of such "blocks."

A hierarchical program can be rigid or flexible. In the former case there is only one order of activation of the "blocks" and of elements in each of them, this being executed independent of conditions. In flexible programs many variants of subprograms are provided on each level; activation of this one or that one is determined by a series of local conditions evaluated on the basis of the feedback. Different degrees of flexibility are possible as a function of the number of possible variants and the number of parameters in direct and feedback connections which are considered in the selection of the optimal variant. Let us dwell on these questions in greater detail.

A general schematic for a hierarchical program with two variants is shown in Fig. 24. This program is realized from "above

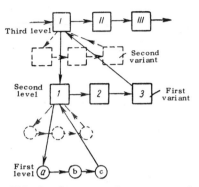

FIG. 24. Schematic of a hierarchical program of activity. Above — coarse stages of complex activity I, II, III. Several stages of sequential activities 1, 2, 3 are activated from each of these. There are two variants (dotted and continuous lines). On the first level there are models of several movements *a*, *b*, *c*, which make up the motor act (several variants of these are also possible).

downwards." Excitation activates it through a model of the first stage I on a higher level. Immediately it descends to a second level and activates block I after which it is directed to the first level, thus activating movement *a*. If we suppose that this is the lowest level, then the program in it is realized by the sequential activation of movement *b*, and then *c*. Here it is ended; the signal about this is sent along a feedback path to the second level, again to block I. Arrival of the signal switches the program of the second level to the following stage, and block 2 begins to operate. From it come actuating signals which descend downwards to the first stage by which a corresponding program is activated and developed. A signal about its termination activates block 3 on the second level. Returning from it to the first level the signals initiate the next program. Block 3 will be informed of its completion, but since there are no programs beyond this on this level the signal will move to the third level, to a model of stage I. This completes the execution of the first stage and stage II is now activated. Its program develops in the same order—sequentially on all levels. The general program will end when on a higher (a third) level, all three of its stages are executed in full and the corresponding signals will have arrived from a lower level. All this is a description of a simple hierarchical program. Feedback connections are depicted here only in the form of signals about the completion of the corresponding hierarchical program.

Of course, real programs are much more complex than their schematic representations.

First of all, generally there are several variants of programs which exist at intermediate levels. This means that the same motor act can be realized by different movements. For example: depending on the circumstance we turn a key to the right or the left or even in some other way. Generally, there is a most suitable variant and this one is activated first. If its execution runs into difficulties then the next variant in order of having been "paved" will be activated, and so forth. To attain such an order, it is essential to have information about the preparedness of all subprograms. This is supplied by the feedback and is taken into account upon activation of each stage. It is necessary to dwell on this in greater detail.

Besides a program for the direct activation of one level after another there exists a large "system of service," without which any program would not be executed. It activates a different type of receptor, connections, and informational systems of the servo type. A servosystem is a model of a program in which different information about its execution is reflected and compared with that which is required and expected. We can separately identify at least three types of servosystems:

1. A servosystem which registers execution of control signals. This system is primarily represented by the receptors in muscles and joints which signal concerning time, displacements, and stresses. These signals go upwards and are compared with the "proper ones"—with that copy of the basic program by which the stages are activated. If the program is well-trained, then the starting and regulating signals are exactly measured-out and are easily corrected by feedback signals from the working organs. As an example of the realization of such a program, consider a man writing with closed eyes or in darkness. A similar system must exist on each level. On the lower levels, it follows the sequencing of movements, compares them with the proper ones and remembers the process of their execution (for example, how each letter is written). On the middle level, it determines the execution of the stage (that is, which letters have already been written). Still higher, execution of stages of operation are noted. This is a system of regulation according to the situation of the working organs. Thus speech is regulated in the deaf or writing in the blind.

2. A servosystem which operates according to effect, according to result. Every activity embraces some result expressed in another code and not in terms of muscular movements. For example, in writing it is not only movement (which is important for the first system) but also the configuration of letters written on the paper. Speech is not only movement of muscles of the larynx and the chest, but also oscillations of the air—the sound. This relates even more to complex operating tasks—things are their derivatives. Naturally, the result of the activity may be sensed by other sense organs, by receptors, and compared with a form which exists in the informational part of the brain—with a model, which, generally speaking, was already envisaged upon activation of the corresponding program (see Fig. 23). If the first system functions on any lower level, then the second operates on a higher level, when as a consequence of the completion of a specific stage of activity a unit of a new code is formulated (for example, a letter or a word)—a result which can be sensed, remembered in temporary memory, and identified by means of comparison.

3. Finally, still another servosystem exists—the system of feelings. Each movement is reflected in the feeling sphere, since it is accompanied by the reception of information from the organs of movement (resistance, weight, fatigue, and even pain). The reception of the result also has reflection in the feeling sphere. According to the general rules of subjectivity, feelings depend on the adjustment of the internal state of the organism and not merely

on the operation itself or its results. A model of feelings which are expected to occur in the course of execution of programs is, in general, also known, although, possibly, not so precisely as a model of movements or a model-image of the result. But this system, very likely exists at a higher level, since it utilizes information from the former and determines a very important parameter—the energy of the activity. It may also give a signal for its cessation.

The work of all three types of servosystem is directed to the obtaining of that effect which has been assumed on the first stage— in the planning of the activity and the selection of the program. For this they must possess an image or model of that which is required and in turn receive that which was obtained as a result. All these activities are executed by the very same apparatus described above. It is for just this reason that one cannot isolate programs of sensing and information processing from the overall program of activity.

Servosystems operate as a result of the comparison of the real and the intended, obtaining the concurrence or disagreement in quantitative form. This is discerned by special programs of information processing, elicits certain feelings, these in turn constitute desires which determine the selection of programs of amplification or simply for regulation of stress. Similar situations can also arise when there is a radical change of program, either in its entirety or in relation to certain hierarchical subprograms. If the discord is so great that it is impossible to correct for it, corresponding feelings and desires arise and the program ceases.

Every servosystem embraces foresight. Properly, an element of this occurs even on the first stage. Experience is its source— operations which have taken place in the past under the same or similar conditions. One can consider that as soon as the program has been activated on the very first stage, all of its succeeding links—both in the form of models of the sequence of activation and in models of servosystems—have already come into some excitation and their energy potential has been increased. This is its own kind of preparation, some kind of readiness. Of course, it is different on different levels. The higher the level, the greater the segment of time required for such "planning" since the temporary memory is longer in the entire system serving it.

While man goes about making something, he holds an image of the item to be produced in an excited state, and this at a high level. Lower levels, which have been called upon to accomplish only a contraction of some groups of muscles, are notified only shortly before the activation of the program. To notify long before is senseless, since servosystems of a corresponding level are not structured so as to remember their own assignment for a prolonged period of time.

Excitation of the whole future program of activities represents, in essence, a program of the imagination. If only the higher level is activated it "runs through" the program very quickly—the program and its results are represented in general features in the course of a short segment of time. It is natural that all temporal laws are violated in this. If we present a program in detail, that is, with the inclusion of lower-level models and their subprograms, then this will take more time for review but in general this will still be much less than its actual execution. It happens that activities are conceived in a reduced tempo. I will not dwell on this question at this time since it will be illuminated below.

Nevertheless, imagination always occurs upon realization of any program, even in animals. This fulfulls a practical need—it activates certain preliminary programs, while this is usually done automatically. Such preparation relates to both the lower links of muscles which have to operate and to the organism as a whole, this in relation to an increase in the productivity of the organs of breathing, circulation, and the general increase in the tones of the lower regulating systems.

The flexibility of a program is not only a function of the possibility of selecting variants of subprograms on lower levels in conformance with conditions on the periphery. An opposite mechanism also exists, as when there are also certain models on a higher level and lower ones are selected taking into account that the entire combination of these upper ones will be satisfied. The mechanism of such a selection is illustrated by the schematic in Fig. 25. Each variant of a subprogram at a lower level, represented by its own models, has connections with several models at the upper level. One of these is the main one. The integrated energy of each such program at a lower level is determined by the entire complex of influences from the programs at the upper level. When selection of a variant of a subprogram occurs on the basis of an aspect of the main upper program then, other things being equal, that is, in the absence of direct prohibition from the periphery (suppose that

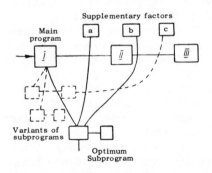

FIG. 25. Schematic for the selection of an optimum subprogram as a function of the main program and supplementary factors (codes-qualities). I, II, III are stages of the main program.

the operating organs which must take part in this subprogram and are occupied with the execution of another program), that variant is selected which has the highest energy. Thus, supplementary factors can influence the selection of a concrete variant of a program.

It is well known, that the same task can be performed by different men in different ways, this as a function of the requirements which the individuals present to themselves. A thing may be made slowly or quickly, well or carelessly, handsomely, precisely, and so forth. Many similar qualities exist, each of which to some degree determines the program of those movements which result in production of the item. There is a general structure to the item—an image of it exists in the cortex; this determines the main model of the program. Enumerated supplementary qualities may also exist—these being supplementary codes in the information processing. These impose specific distinctions on the variant of the program.

It is especially important to consider energy. The speed of execution or the "force" used in overcoming difficulties encountered in work depends on the level of energy of all models which participate in the realization of the given program. It is just this in the final analysis which determines the frequency of nerve impulses which are directed to the muscle and which elicits the power developed by it. The level of energy is determined by the basic stimulus, which was designated in the description of the first stage as desire. It is the function of the force of that feeling which activates the whole program (reference F_1 in Fig. 23). But there may be several desires in the execution of the work. The main one is to make an item. Supplementary to this, there may be the desire to make it very quickly or with great precision. These very desires determine the energy of supplementary models—of factors which influence the selection of variants of subprograms (see Fig. 25).

A model of a program, after integration of all factors on a higher level, is represented in several forms. First of all, it is a sequence of activities, represented in stages. Further, it is reflected in models of those servosystems which control execution of the programs. This relates to all three types of servosystems, but particularly to the first and the second (systems of movements and of results). Feelings determine the energy level of the whole program.

Models are certainly not frozen and unalterable. Their flexibility depends not only on the abundance of variants at lower levels but also on the many-aspectedness of influences from "above" which determine the selection of some of these variants. A model of a program is formed anew each time. Simultaneously with this its "stamp" takes the form of reference base models which are stored as matrices in servosystems. Thus, execution of the programs is ensured in conformance with preset conditions.

But not always.

Quite frequently failures occur. If the program is not executed as conceived, the discord is revealed by a second servosystem, this being reflected in terms of unpleasant feelings. After this the program is improved or it will not be engaged the next time.

Accumulated experience forms a basis for the improvement of programs. This is achieved as the results of each activity are remembered and corrections are introduced into the model of the program. The mechanism of this phenomenon is precisely the same as those changes of the models-standards in permanent memory as a result of the accumulation of experience of information processing. In servosystems there is a model of a program of each level. During completion of a motor act, the actual execution of the program is imprinted in temporary memory and to some insignificant degree this is reflected in the permanent model of the program, that is, it moves into prolonged memory. This relates to all three types of servosystems, but possibly, in the greatest measure to the one which concerns feeling. If nonexecution of a program is accompanied by very unpleasant feelings, then they are remembered and upon repeated activation this former failure lowers the changes of the given variant of the program in a substantial way (through change of feeling F_3 in the already depicted schematic in Fig. 23).

The question as to how new programs of activities are formed is very important. Actually a child is born completely "without programs"—does not know how to do anything and must learn everything. In lesser animals the situation is not this bad— models of their motor acts are stored from birth in the subcortex or possibly in the lower levels of the cortex. As soon as the appropriate cells mature, sometimes within several weeks following birth, a motor act is automatically ready. Future development simply improves this to some degree.

The reflex of imitation is the basis for the training of movements. As already mentioned, its essence is in the program of computation—of automatic activation of activities which computate sound or visual image. At first this is done involuntarily, and then with the attraction of consciousness. Of course, imitation is sometimes initially unsuccessful. Only after many attempts and errors is a particular program of operations developed, it being reflected in servosystems. Everything is based on the retention of each attempt together with concomitant feelings. Successful experiences enter memory with positive feelings, unsuccessful attempts enter with negative ones. Upon subsequent activation preference is given to the positive feelings. A necessary condition for training is the presence in memory of a pattern—of an image-model of the strange motor act so as to permit comparison with its own act, giving to the results an evaluation in terms of a corresponding feeling. An illustrative schematic of such training is depicted in Fig. 26.

There is an image of the strange motor act in the memory. It is computed by the reflex of imitation and the man (the child) tries to reproduce it. The excitation for such an attempt can be the reflex itself or a compulsion from the environment. The result of the particular activity is imprinted in the temporary memory of the first, and particularly of the second servosystems. Then a comparison is made of the formed image with the strange standard. In case of satisfactory or even of reasonable coincidence, satisfaction develops—excitation of the "pleasure" center. Such a movement goes into memory with a plus sign. At the same time it is stored in the servosystem of the motor sphere. Thus it is that positive experience is stored in memory. Subsequently, this is repeated many times and gradually the motor act develops to maximum perfection.

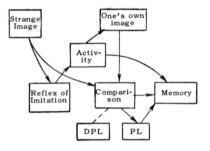

FIG. 26. Schematic of the education process using the imitation reflex and remembering successful trials selected through feelings.

There is yet another example of training: suppose the teacher guides the hand of a pupil while copying letters or a drawing. In this case the image of the program is stored in the first servosystem in the form of memory of impulses which arrive from muscles, joints and tendons.

Thus, programs of elementary motor acts are created as a result of utilization of the reflex mechanism of imitation and of both servosystems. Subsequently, complex and prolonged activities are built from these "bricks." With this the levels accumulate—in some people to a greater and in others to a lesser extent.

Perhaps we should continue our explanation as to the source of successful movements. An error in the execution of a program can turn out to be beneficial, it may even be accompanied by a pleasant feeling and remain in memory. Frequently, we observe how it is that out of a large number of redundant and frequently random movements of a child, successful forms of behavior are sifted out. The high motor activity of children and young animals promotes the selection of successful programs which are generated as a result.

The reflex of imitation is not limited to the computation of simple movements. It extends even to complex programs. It is possible that the independent play of children is an attempt to reproduce the complex programs of the domestic life and professional activity of adults.

Speech is a product of both the development of the mind and its stimuli. Using the concepts of cybernetics; speech is a coding for the transmission of information, in other words, a means of communication between people. Words form a universal code by which we can transmit almost any information, although this may be far from economic and frequently produces great distortion. Writing is a physical model of speech which permits the storage and transmission of information. Currently there are still other technological means for achieving this goal; as, for example, sound transcription.

Speech plays a great role in education. In point of fact, the majority of higher-meaning concepts—of higher codes produced from concrete images of the external world—are exceedingly unclear. Only with the help of words are they concretized. Therefore, in the course of training, frequently the name of the concept is first taught and only after this is it decoded. An initially indistinct concept is gradually concretized in the process of acquisition of experiencé by man, as it were, crystallizing in the word.

We have already mentioned the role of speech in the self-organization of higher levels of the cortex—of the associative fields (see Fig. 15). The paths "upwards" are paved because of random coincidences of excitation of cells of the upper level (the abstract concept) and cells of the lower levels in which models of concrete images are reflected. If the situation "below" is complex, then it is very difficult to repeat it precisely "above." But if paths from complex and not very specific models intersect with paths from a model of a word in a cell of an upper level, then it becomes quite simple to condition this connection.

However, it is unnecessary to identify speech with thought. The capacity to understand higher codes of information (complex systems) is determined by the presence of higher levels in the cortex which integrate information and not by the simple replacement of concrete concepts by their word equivalents. Even a deaf-mute can think without knowing words, but his thinking is much poorer than the thought of a normal individual and is developed only because within human society there are other codes besides words— mimicry, movement, things.

The essence of speech rests on the potential for realizing parallel programs of information processing. One program processes models of concrete images, a second, processes models of their word equivalents. A third program is even possible—a motor one, in which sound images of words are computed and are reproduced by a motor code.

Words are abstract equivalents of concrete images. An associative connection is easily established between models of certain ones and others according to the general principles of coincidence in time of two excited models. It is just in this way that we learn to speak. Possibly, there are not just two, but many parallel models, as, for example, when there is knowledge of several languages or the existence of codes of drawings, symbols, formulas, along with words.

Primary information, transmitted by words, can also be developed according to hierarchical programs as can information from concrete images. In fact this might even offer superior performance, and this at greater convenience. In the same way, several levels of meaning codes are generated for images or events including main ones and supplementary ones—and the formation of complex codes is also possible in this same way. (See Fig. 14.)

Consider the pronunciation of words or, more accurately, a story comprised of phrases—here is a typical hierarchical motor program: at the higher levels is located a model of ideas, lower there are levels of meaning "blocks," then lower, programs for the pronounciation of words, and still lower—for sounds. A particular phrase is selected from many variants on the basis of the presence of other supplementary feelings and of desires (see Fig. 15). Very likely, such a schematic is most appropriate to the motor programs of speech.

It is generally known that the identity of two models can be demonstrated by an exhaustive comparison of their details. Identification can take place more quickly but the result may not be so precise. I will attempt to explain how this occurs.

Almost every word has several meanings. By means of the synaptic connections having different resistance its model is coupled with many models of concrete images or with models on the meaning levels of phrases. There is a hierarchy of the penetrability of connections, as a result there is a first meaning for the word, a second, a third, and so on. The word may, by certain of its meanings, very precisely correspond to a concrete image—most frequently this relates to the names of objects. For others, the image equivalent may be quite indistinct. Generally, this relates to qualities, to abstract concepts—to that which we call supplementary codes. Thus, the word "quick" designates a quality of a moving object or person but, at the same time, is a feature of the character as well—the capability for quick decisions, for high-speed reactions.

Thus it is possible to very quickly describe complex events, through use of the approximate meanings of words, of course, with a loss of information. The whole secret is that between levels there are many crossing connections. More precisely: a model at a higher level of meaning can be connected with a model at a lower level of another analyzer, as, for example, with a model of a word. Thus, the concrete image-concept "war" is very complex, but its model has a direct connection with a model of the word "war" which is situated somewhere on the second level above models of sounds. A corresponding schematic is shown in Fig. 27. Thus, a brief description of complex events is possible thanks to the availability of these "diagonal" connections and approximate meanings of words.

At the moment when a person observes something, hierarchial information processing occurs in his cerebral cortex, in the sphere of concrete visual images. However, simultaneously with these images and their high-meaning levels—images-models of words or of short phrases are also excited, in precisely the same manner as models of feelings are excited. In other words, information is reprocessed immediately in several parallel programs which influence one another.

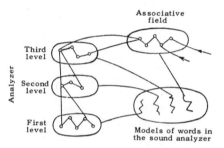

FIG. 27. Schematic of "diagonal" connections of models of words with hierarchical models of concrete information.

The excitation of models of words and phrases in the information processing is generally expressed by motor rather than by a feeling program. In other words, when a picture is sensed, there is a simultaneous mental pronounciation of the words which describe it—as though the listeners hear them spoken from inside. Consequently, the main program of speech is "motor" not "feeling." A person at first learns to speak and only then to think with words.

Learning the pronunciation of words occurs according to the schematic shown in Fig. 26. Due to the instinct of imitation, a child retrieves sounds from his memory, comparing his own pronunciation with that of others. Gradually this improves, until finally he ceases to note the technology of pronunciation per se.

Switching from the feeling program to the motor program is realized according to the general reflex of self-expression. A feeling must always be expressed by some motor reaction. Only with the passage of time does a person train himself to suppress it—to convert it into thoughts. But I believe that he never completely succeeds in doing this. Thoughts are these same activities, but very strongly inhibited. Investigating the biotics of the musculature of the speech apparatus, it is possible to get information about unpronounced words—their biotics are too weak to elicit contraction of muscles but in every other way they are the same as in conversation.   Further, small children converse uninterruptedly. Their speech is incorrect, nonsequential, disconnected, because it directly reflects the activation of motor programs from the feeling images they receive or recall. With time this passes, but even as adults we catch ourselves whispering our own thoughts. We will discuss thinking in more detail below, but here we are interested in the programs of speech, and in the way they are formed.

Speech as an activity may be explained in terms of the same stages as other activity, such as work with our hands. First, a stimulus is required with which the activity is associated. In a discussion this may take the form of a question, in a report it takes the form of an idea and the necessity to express it. Frequently joint activity of an entire complex of stimuli "compels speaking," that is, activates a corresponding program.

Figure 28 offers an illustrative schematic for the formation of a program of response to the speech of a fellow conversationalist. At first this speech is remembered in temporary memory. Then it is analyzed according to two programs:

1. Meaning—according to general principles of hierarchical information processing with the generation and storage in temporary memory of hierarchical codes. Several supplementary codes are also generated. Of these one is especially important. It concerns the form of speech—whether it represents a question, order, request, or permission.

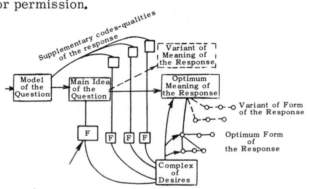

FIG. 28. Schematic of formation of the program of response. From a model of a question, its meaning and codes-qualities are generated. All these models are associated with the feelings (F), which then form a complex of desires. Several variants of meaning and forms of response correspond to the meaning of the question. The optimum variants for the given situation is selected because of the influences of the complex of desires.

2. Feeling—with which feelings the speech is associated, both with respect to the main and supplementary codes. Speech can elicit an entire range of feelings.

An answer is readied as a result of analysis according to the general principles of switching from models of sensed information to a program of activity. At first the idea of the answer develops, that is, its higher level in which the influences of all meaning codes are considered, this being isolated from the speech of the partner—both from the main and of the supplementary codes.

The character of the realization of a program for response, that is, its form (brevity, detail, rapidity, slowness, crudity, politeness, and other qualities), is determined by a selection of variants of expression through the interaction of ideas of response with a complex of desires which are, in turn, the consequence of a complex of feelings.

For the time being, this concerns only the planning of the response in content and form. It can be propagated to the very lowest levels when a person pronounces in words his entire speech in his mind, senses it with servosystems and corrects it through the feeling sphere of one of the systems. The plan of the response can be very brief, that is, it can remain in the sphere of higher levels. For example, it may be formulated as follows: "I will now answer, briefly, and sharply," whereupon this phrase is not pronounced—it is in an upper level where the thought does not require verbal form. In such a case very little time is required to plant the response.

The next state can also be brief or prolonged—estimating the reaction of the partner or listener. The effect from the conjectured response "is played back" to a model of the partner. Fundamentally, this is reduced to an identification of the feelings of the partner, but it is even possible to guess the degree of his understanding of the meaning of the given response. On the basis of the corresponding conclusion, a prediction is made of the response of the partner.

Another stage—consideration of the reaction to the future response of the partner, primarily to the feeling as, for example ("I will speak sharply to him. He will be indignant and may answer with rudeness. How shall I react to this? Am I frightened? Then I had better soften my speech"). Once more the planned speech (the response) is corrected relative to the possible reaction.

Only after this is the program finally activated: levels begin to "work," and the content of the speech is expressed in words.

However, observation of effect goes on even in the course of pronouncing the speech, thus corrections can be introduced both in its content and form as a function of the effect.

Such is the general schematic of the motor program of speech. For more precise modeling (understanding) of it, it is necessary to introduce the concept of consciousness.

4

Consciousness, Thinking, Creativity

Programs of consciousness and subconsciousness. It is difficult to define consciousness in a few words. One may characterize both physiological and psychological aspects of consciousness in terms of the following factors:

1. The active function of mechanisms of attention-amplification. These mechanisms ensure the generation of basic stimuli (of the main channels of communication) from the general stream of external and internal information circulating within the cerebral cortex at any given moment.

2. The formation and active function of the complex of models of the "I," itself. These models include sensations emanating from all parts of the organs sensory systems. The models are compared to the flow of information which enters from the external environment, this being sensed by remote receptors such as the organs of hearing, sight, and smell.

3. A proper evaluation of the interrelationships of external and internal stimuli (concerning their relations to the subject matter). This amounts to a specification of the reality of the subject in the surrounding environment.

4. The formation of mechanisms of self-observation and self-control; that is, of memory imprinting of one's own behavior and its evaluation in terms of a comparison with specified models which, in turn, are derived from training and education.

5. Formation and activity of the mechanisms of the will (see below).

6. The sensation of time and voluntary transfer of attention to the past, the present, or to the future.

Consciousness is a heterogeneous and "multistage" concept. One can separately identify its various stages, as follows:

1. Activity of mechanisms of attention-amplification.

2a. Separation (evaluation of the interrelations) of external and internal stimuli; that is, specifying one's self within the surrounding environment.

114

b. Orientation with respect to time.

c. Formation of models of the "I," itself, this being the simplest self-observation and control. The will is viewed in relation to the control of activity.

3. Deepened self-analysis (observations of thoughts) and concentration; that is, the willful control of thoughts. Of course, such characterization is completely conditional. The different stages of consciousness can be observed in the development of a child, and in some of the physiological and pathological conditions of the nervous system.

Higher animals possess the first stage of consciousness, and possibly stage 2a as well. Small children stand at the very same level. Adults go through various stages but do not necessarily reach the last stage. All stages of consciousness, beginning with 2b, are a consequence of the influence of human society, of training, and of education.

Let us dwell on the first stage of consciousness—the programs of attention.

Information enters the brain simultaneously along many channels. Models of a large number of motor programs are stored in the cortex. For expeditious activity of the organism, these programs should not interfere with one another in the process of their execution, but, of course, two simultaneous activities cannot proceed without there being some loss in the effectiveness of each. At the same time, the system must be prepared for an immediate change of the programs of operation, this as a function of new, more powerful stimuli entering from other channels.

Thus, in a very complex system, there must be a program for switching among the various streams of sensed information and motor programs. This function is attributed to consciousness in man. It is thought that when alert and receptive to external stimuli, man consciously selects that particular course of action which will deliver the greatest satisfaction to him. It is believed that animals do not possess consciousness and that their actions are directed by instinct; in our terminology, the stimulus, external or internal, automatically activates each program.

This concept is justified for lower animals. The diversity of information they sense is not great and the selection of motor programs is limited; but even these lower animals have a specific subordination of stimuli and programs. Their mechanisms of interrelations provide expedient activity in different periods of their life cycle.

Higher animals, especially those having a cortex, have much greater diversity and, therefore, possess a program for selection which guarantees the execution of a prime motor act at the expense of excluding others.

This is realized with the help of the attention mechanism (Fig. 29). The essence of this mechanism, in general outline, consists of the following: One of the many channels along which information may enter in any given moment is amplified and all other channels are suppressed. In other words, one motor program is amplified while all other motor programs are inhibited. Most probably the function of this amplifier is carried out by the reticular formation.   Amplification cannot be applied to a particular model for any significant duration.   The mechanisms are such that the amplifying system rapidly fatigues and requires switching-over to another channel.   However, the system quickly gathers "strength" and can then return to the former model, but again for only a short duration.   This mechanism is biologically very important since it guarantees the possibility of reevaluating the significance of information entering the system in brief time intervals and, as a function of this reevaluation, the switching of the program of activity.

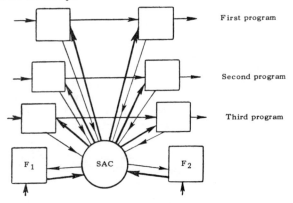

FIG. 29. Schematic illustrating the program of attention. SAC has direct and reverse connections with feeling elements (from the left) and motor elements (from the right) of programs of activities, and also with feelings F_1, F_2. Any of these models can be amplified, the remaining are suppressed during this time.

Attention-amplification can be applied to any cortical model, that is, to information being sensed or the model of a program while this exists at various levels. In this way, models of feelings and sensations can be amplified.

The degree of amplification is determined by the activity of the amplifying system, and this activity is a direct function of the emotional state, that is, of the intensity of feelings, this being the most important regulator of animal behavior. This system fatigues. Turning the system off yields sleep, while extreme suppression yields the anesthesia state. There exists positive feedback between models of feelings and the amplifying system; thus each may amplify the other. Probably the amplifying system is stimulated from the universal "pleasure" and "displeasure" centers.

The program of attention-amplification is a basic attribute of first-stage consciousness. For man, "being conscious" means that he orients himself with respect to his surrounding environment. This also applies to animals. Without attention one cannot imagine all other phenomena of human consciousness.

There are far fewer models in the cortex of animals than in man. This is a function of both the brain structure and the training. Human attention can turn to models of several types:

1. Different channels which sense information—the fact of "hearing," of "looking," of "feeling."

2. Models in corresponding analyzers—the process of recognition of visual or auditory form.

3. Higher levels of these forms—recognition (interpretation) of the entire picture, not merely of a fragment. For example, a motion picture is recognized in terms of several episodes or persons, an opera is recognized by its sounds.

4. Different levels of motor programs—from concepts of the working processes to careful execution of simple movement.

5. Model-forms from the past—recall.

6. Prediction of the future—imagination, dreams.

7. Feelings, sensations, emotions.

8. Sensations from internal organs and from the surface of the body.

Thinking in its most general form consists of a sequential amplification of different models. Thought is an amplified model of a form, an activity, or a feeling—from the present, the past, or the future.

One may evidently liken the mechanism by which attention is switched to a competition between several competing individual models which have been individually excited. A comparison is made as to the magnitude of the potential of the energy in each of these, preférence being given to that one which commands the greatest potential. Consider the following example: let us assume that the first model is excited and amplified by attention. Its excitability is then transmitted by connections to the other models which have been associated with it. In a short time amplification of the first model will die down. The attention must then be switched to another model. At any particular moment and without conscious awareness all models are weakly excited. In the next instant, if there are no strong external stimuli, the most excited model of those associated with the previously amplified one will take possession of attention. In this way a train of thought is generated. Any other model may command attention provided it shows greater excitability at the moment of switching. When this occurs the previous train of thought will be destroyed.

The capability for competing is directly determined by the energy (by the potential) of the excited model corresponding to its value to the organism, this being expressed as the degree of excitability of the feeling sphere elicited by the action of this stimulus or by the recall of this image. Inner stimuli or programs associated with instincts are always the models which have greatest excitation in animals, but in man the most excited models may be abstract ones which have been inculcated by training and which significantly amplify themselves owing to the operation of the "principle of self-amplification." A diagram of sources of energy of a model is shown in Fig. 30. To this must be added the level of particular activity which is a function of the specificity of the cell and of its prior conditioning.

The situation in the cortex at the moment of switching of attention may be quite variable in accordance with the following principles: a) externally; various stimuli operate which excite corresponding models along different channels; b) internally; sensations are operating; c) part of the models in memory is excited by the preceding period of amplification or receive preliminary amplification from other excited models by association. This picture reminds one of a constantly changing relief, in which the hills and valleys "influence" one another. At any given moment one height is much higher than another and in turn this height, by its connections, amplifies other heights via its connections to them. The external activity is amplified by some other factors. At the moment of redistribution, the height is rapidly lowered and there occurs a leveling of all other heights associated with it. Of those amplified in the next go-round only the highest one is excited, it grows sharply and it then almost instantly is again lowered, and this goes on continually.

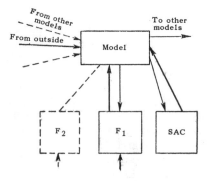

FIG. 30. Schematic which shows sources of specific energy obtained by the model. F_1, F_2 - feelings.

At any given moment only one model is amplified by attention and is located at the level of consciousness. This is the main one; this is the thought. Activity of all other models is much lower but this does not mean that such activity is absent. On the contrary; the reprocessing of information, that is, the movement of excitation from some nerve cells to others, the execution of specific programs embraces all models. Subconsciousness is the processing of information by cortical models which at any given moment are not amplified by attention. For example, one cogitates while one walks. This is execution of a program at the level of consciousness. However, at the same time you are following the road and are controlling your steps. Consequently you are fulfilling a program of movement in all of its complexities. This is going on in the sphere of the subconscious. If you meet some obstacle along the way or if your glance falls upon something novel, consciousness will for some time be transferred.

The "potential" for reprocessing of information at the level of consciousness is high and we may say that this potential determines the speed of reprocessing. But the total quantity of reprocessed information is incomparably greater in the sphere of the subconscious because billions of cells in the subconscious are interacting, perhaps on a lower energy level, but continually. Of course separate programs "work" well when a high frequency of impulses is not required for the transfer of excitation from one cell to another. And so one can perform habitual activities and can at the same time think about something else.

The role of the subconscious is very great: Models are prepared in the subconscious which compete in order to attract attention, that is, are candidates for the level of consciousness. Thus "latent sites of excitation," the "secret thoughts" which disturb man acquire great significance. These take possession of attention as soon as the flow of strong external stimuli becomes weak. In this way the reprocessing of information in the subconscious directs the flow of thought to a significant degree, operating, if we may so express ourselves, "from behind the wings." In the formation of such "latent sites," the measure of participation of instincts and the internal influences, of feelings is particularly great.

Recapitulating the above, the role of the subconscious can be reduced to the following functions:

1. Primary processing of entering information which here, as it were, is prepared for the "conscious level."

2. Many feelings operate through the subconscious level and impart an unrecognized subjectivity to the reprocessed information.

3. Many unconscious movements are activated in the subconscious, provided that they can be "wedged" into conscious programs without loss.

4. At the very same place variants of lower-level motor programs are selected as a function of signals "from below."

5. Complex, but very well-studied movements can be realized on a subconscious level; only their activation and extinction are done consciously.

It would, however, be incorrect to think as Freud thought that consciousness is a simple instrument of the subconscious. This

is only true for lower animals. In man, the matter is quite different. The heart of the matter is that a model, amplified by attention,
imparts powerful impulses to other associated models and in this
way increases their potential, that is, they develop the potential to
take possession of attention at its very first redistribution. In
addition, the previous model still possesses a high potential after
amplification switches to other models, and after a brief rest period
will again be in a state to seize the attention and enter into the
sphere of consciousness.   Moreover, it is necessary to consider
that each such "conscious" period conditions the cell, that is, the
principle of self-amplification goes into operation. Thus if there
are no important distracting stimuli, because of the amplification
in periods of consciousness, the abstracted cortical model of some
external object may be transformed into a "powerful model" and
this model becomes that concealed site which will actively compete
for attention with other models amplified by feelings "from below."

After statement of these general propositions, one must pursue
questions concerning quantitative characteristics of consciousness
and subconsciousness—question concerning their "levels."

First of all, these characteristics are associated. The higher
the amplification of some models, that is, the higher the level of
consciousness, the more suppressed are all remaining models and
the lower their average potential energy (activity).

The general level of consciousness depends upon the activity
of the main "generator of energy"—let this be the reticular formation (RF). In all probability, this level is determined by the cell
programs of corresponding structures, that is, by their statistical
and dynamic characteristics. Of course, one cannot attribute some
self-contained significance to this level of consciousness. The
system amplification control (SAC) operates as an instrument of
determinate programs. The system is activated externally but then
to a significant degree influences the subsequent course of the program.   This is a positive feedback evidently having a large coefficient.

Figure 31 illustrates hypothetical connections of the SAC with
other structures of the subcortex. Evidently, the basic path along
which the SAC is excited is the displeasure center (DPL) and to a
lesser degree the pleasure center (PL).   Centers of emotion are
associated with these, but if these centers are activated they most
probably possess their own path for influencing the SAC. In the
diagram, the descending paths are depicted from the SAC to the
spinal cord and to the trunk centers. I have confined myself only
to the arrow leading to the higher autonomic centers (HAC) which
change the entire tuning of the internal sphere of the first three
regulating systems.   In the given case, the increase of activity of
the adrenal system (the adrenal gland) is particularly important
because adrenalin is produced which exerts a positive inverse
activity on the reticular formation-system amplification control

(RF-SAC).   Activation of the hormonal element significantly pro-
longs the time of excitation.   A basic path for stimulation of the
SAC is via the feeling sphere but other paths may also be significant: directly from cortical models, provided their spontaneous
activity is sharply increased as a consequence of conditioning and
hypertrophy.   These models can represent completely abstract
phenomena or programs.   A second path is from centers of complex reflexes: "What is this?," aims, freedoms. True, these influences probably are less strong, but, on the other hand, they are
more prolonged and stable.

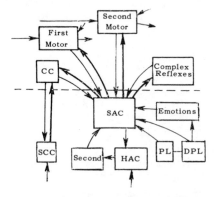

FIG. 31. Connections of the SAC with
other structures of the cortex and
subcortex.   CC – Cortical center of
feelings.   SCC – Subcortical center of
feelings.

The connection between the intensity of excitability of the models
which have been switched into "consciousness" and the suppression of "the subconscious level," and also the schematic of the SAC
itself are depicted in Fig. 32.   Naturally, one may consider this
only in an informational way.   The system consists of two "generators"—excitation and suppression, connected to each other
by means of feedback.   The switch is depicted which directs the
energy of excitation into one selected channel, that is, to the model
activated into "consciousness."   The channels of all other models
are automatically connected to the suppression generator.   The
switch is operated periodically in accordance with some temporal
law, but the angle chosen is selected by a special comparatory
system which collates the potentials of energy of all connected
models at all times (a "counter").
    We will endeavor to represent the activity of the cortex under
different degrees of amplification-suppression.
    Let us assume that the excitation of the SAC is very great as,
for example, under emotions or strong feelings. In this case the
potential of energy of "recognized" models is quite great and all

other models are strongly suppressed. Consequently, the excited models receive the most powerful push, that is, a significant amount of energy.   I have already mentioned a hypothetical law of the SAC: the higher the excitation, the greater the energy transmission, the more quickly the connection from the switch to the model fatigues.   As a result the amplification begins to decrease but, on the other hand, the suppression is also decreased. While this occurs, the particular energy of an earlier amplified model remains high and this energy strives to move via the more well-worn connections to other models connected with the first model by stable associations.   These can be models of activities or of other forms of reprocessing of information.   One of them either

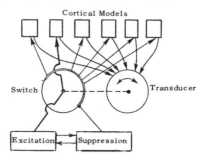

FIG. 32. Conventional schematic of
SAC generators.

receives more energy from the others or its particular activity up to this point in time has been higher, but to the extent of the reduction of the suppressing central influence, it is excited all the more strongly.   A system which compares potentials makes a calculation and as soon as the excitability of a second model surpasses the level of the first, the switch will turn to the second model.   It then receives amplification from the generator along a fresh connection.   All remaining models are proportionately suppressed. The very same thing then happens with this second model. The connector to it fatigues, the energy of excitation which is being transmitted drops, and the suppressing influence on all other models simultaneously decreases.   But the push received by the second model may have been sufficiently strong so that it transfers its own still high energy content along well-worn paths to a third model.   This process continues, the most characteristic feature being that excitation can be transferred along a limited circle of models since after the third or fourth switch-over, the particular activity of the first model, having itself at one time received a strong impetus, will again grow and the model again seizes amplification attention.   Thus the circle is closed.   It is true that in periods of switch-over, attention can wander into byways but if there are no closed connections (that is, they are blind alleys), then attention will again return to the former circle of models. In life this is what happens: in periods of strong emotions or stress, the circle of thought is not great, and the attention continually returns to problems which serve as the rationale for this excitation. An illustrative schematic of such a phenomenon is shown in Fig. 33.

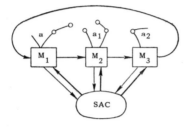

FIG. 33. Schematic of cyclic switching of attention. M_1, M_2, M_3 — Cortical models; a, a_1, a_2 — "dead ends"

If the level of excitation is moderate, for example, if interest is low, a closed circle of models cannot exist but the excitability of one model remains high and attention periodically returns to that model, although the digressive excursion will be longer and deeper.

The excitation of the SAC cannot long endure. The higher its level of excitation, the briefer the periods of its activity. Evidently, this is associated with losses of some substances. Following a rise there occurs a decline, and then a second wave, already reduced, becomes possible. Long periods of increased activity may occur, such as tension-producing creative work carried on over many days, but following this, fatigue develops and the capacity for work declines. Some reserves may be exhausted from the second level of cells in the SAC. Daily sleep is very important in connection with this in that it serves as the necessary time of rest for the amplifying system and for all cells of the cortex and possibly for the entire organism.

The level of consciousness also determines the level of subconsciousness, that is, the degree of suppression of all models in the cortex which do not directly participate in programs of consciousness. Figure 34 shows how the excitation might fluctuate under different stresses of attention, that is, under sharp excitation of the SAC and with lower excitation. We can assume that in the first case the minimum is high and therefore only models with great activity—usually from within that circle mentioned above, can "break through" into consciousness. Excitation quickly passes from one model to another (surely the connections with the SAC quickly fatigue), but the great quantity of energy transmitted from the excited model promotes rapid excitation of the secondary model.

On the other hand, without high activity of the SAC, the oscillations of excitation are relatively slow and its minimal and maximal levels are low. It follows that even the suppression of all the remaining cortex is significant.

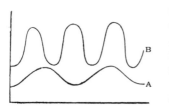

FIG. 34. Variations of the degree of activity of the SAC. A—in the resting state; B—under emotional stress.

All these arguments have a direct relation to the activity of the sphere of the subconscious, that is, to its level. If suppression is low, then the value of information reprocessing in the subconscious is high, and vice versa.

The activity of cells of models in the subconscious is determined by the following factors:

1. The spontaneous activity of cells, which in turn depends on previous conditioning ("the degree of self-amplification") and of the innate characteristics which are different for cells of different cortical structures.

2. Excitations which arise externally, that is, from receptors. Perception of the external world via the very same channels even when attention is not devoted to them although, of course, to a significantly lesser degree.

3. Excitations coming from within the body, via connections with cortical representations of feelings which are being excited from the subcortex, that is, from basic centers.

4. Energy entering from neighboring cell models—along well-worn paths.

5. The degree of suppression which originates from the SAC.

It is known that cells in the cortex are organized into "models"—structures which are united by well-worn connections which reflect information. Therefore, the operation of cells in the subconscious cannot be considered as isolated activity. Frequent or infrequent impulses are propagated along well-worn connections of internally well-organized models, and between them if these connections have little resistance. The excitation of some cells is transmitted to others within the model. As a result, therefore, the entire model is excited. Every cell influences others by direct feedback. It is doubtful that each cell participates in many models, but the "unorganized" propagation of excitation does not proceed in response to this feedback alone. Everything "illuminates" the model, although not strongly. In all probability some kind of local suppression occurs which arises from a moderately excited model in the subconscious, "overemphasizing" it over its neighbors. This is the "negative induction" which was discovered by Pavlov in his time. It is true that there might be no such local mechanism, and that induction may be explained by the suppressing activity of the SAC-RF. However, this problem is not the principal one.

The excitation of a model does not remain internal to the model; once it reaches a determined level, it begins to propagate along well-worn connections to other models. In this way the reprocessing of information in the sphere of the subconscious is explained. It is realized by the very same programs that are in the conscious: hierarchical processing, and the movement to other models along associated connections. It goes without saying that the greatest portion of reprocessing is limited by the number of well-worn connections, consequently this occurs only on lower levels.

The activation of motor programs in the subconscious is encumbered because it demands a high activity of models of feelings and desires. However, it occurs in that case when those connections "work" which are held from birth. As an example, with the unconditioned reflex of scratching, the motor act begins right in the subconscious, and only its results—sensation is "recognized" provided the setting is suitable. If attention itself is concentrated on something else, the entire reflex remains in the subconscious.

There is still another type of subconscious activity—acquired but well-developed movements. As a rule, these are activated in the sphere of consciousness and then are continued in the subconscious. The amplifying system provides the initial impetus, a charge of energy which suffices for the entire period of the activity. As an example, we can refer to the process of walking. Only its beginning is a conscious act, then, if the road is a good one and one has something else to think about, consciousness is transferred. We do not think about our walking although we are controlling our movements continuously. Consciousness only periodically returns to the act of walking and is primarily occupied with something else.

In connection with the possibility of activating movements from within the subconscious, the question arises concerning feedback signaling as to the "preoccupation" of one or another working neuron which directly controls the muscles. A muscle which is already participating in another motor act cannot be switched-in. We have already mentioned such feedback signaling. Evidently, it is distributed in more than one direction, that is, upwards to a higher level of a given program, as well as to models of other programs in which a given muscle may participate. Under these conditions an engaged working cell in one program can no longer be switched-in to another program even if it is not functioning but rather only getting ready for action, for example, as in foresight.

Special conditions of activity in the subconscious sphere originate during sleep when the RF is suppressed, or almost switched-off. The results are manifest in dreams. However, this is a special topic connected with the problem of higher levels of consciousness.

The human program of consciousness is not limited to the mechanism of attention. This is only the programs first stage. Unfortunately, ideas regarding subsequent stages are more obscure. I will attempt to state them as I myself understand them.

In all probability man's higher consciousness has a particular structure in the brain, even though we cannot represent it in the form of some delimited area. Nevertheless, upon consideration of behavior in an informational way, anatomy has a secondary meaning. I believe that consciousness is a supplementary level or indeed several levels of information processing which impart a new quality, that is, social behavior, creativity, and labor, which are particular distinguishing features of the human animal. In these levels the very same types of programs operate as in lower levels. Their fundamental peculiarity lies in the absence or insufficiency of connections utilized from birth. Self-organization prevails here. Speech plays a basic role in the formation of higher concepts. At first the child mechanically memorizes words conforming to the reflex of imitation and then attaches concrete images to them. Furthermore, at the same time the child makes abstract concepts concrete in the form of words. This process is realized under the constant control of the environment. Words are associated with feelings. Some of them are hypertrophied from the "principles of self-amplification" exerting a direct influence on the further development of the intellect.

As has already been indicated, consciousness is an entire complex of programs. We will dwell on these in some detail. The most important of these are the models of "I" and "not-I."

It is known that children for quite some time address themselves in the third person. Only gradually does the child train himself to employ the short word "I." At first the child repeats this pronoun without any thought. Adults correct him and the model "I" establishes broad associations, first of all, with models of feelings, desires, and activities: "I want," "I do," "I am cold," after this the model is strongly hypertrophied because it is connected with the very important subcortical programs "for one's self," that is, with the instinct of self-preservation. The model becomes the embodiment of the self-preservation.

In a parallel way models of the "not I" are formulated as are models of the second person "thou," "you," and the third person "he" and "she." In some languages these words apply only to people, all remaining living things and objects being designated by the word "it."

Ideas concerning the feelings of third persons do not come easily. A child is taught over a long period of time that "Mama is ill," "The dog is ill," until he learns to model others and to identify their feelings with his own. External expression of feelings, that is, mimicry, gestures, and conduct are signals by which the feelings of others are discerned. Nevertheless, even animals possess this quality; they distinguish the emotions of their "companions" according to their external manifestations. Mimicking is an ancient reflection of self-expression. However, animals sense the emotions of another animal only as an unconditioned signal for their own activities while man transfers these emotions to himself, "gains insight" into them, and thus has an opportunity to guess the conduct of a companion in response to his own activities.

Orientation in time is a second very important concept which enters into the complex of consciousness. I will not dwell on concepts of space since these concepts are formulated quite early in man and are well developed in animals. But time is a purely human "acquisition." A child does not become time-oriented for quite some time. An exact notion about time comes only with a precise differentiation of different temporal categories, that is, the second, the minute, the hour, and so forth.

Concepts of the present, the future, and the past are formulated through the system of speech and terminology. The present is most easily associated with the perception of the surrounding environment at any given time. This is the "now" of the child. It is sufficient to attach attention to temporary memory, to receptors, to realize the "now." Concepts such as "in this year," and "in this decade," in other words, reference to the specific past, are established with much greater difficulty. In the English language there are corresponding grammatical differentiations but these do not exist in the Russian language.

The past, in principle, is information which has been stored in permanent memory. However, if the event has just occurred, it is still imprinted in the form of a temporary model—an excitation of a cell complex, and for the time being it is unknown whether or not this excitation will be transferred into permanent memory. There are some very general concepts of the past as, for example, "was" and "happened." These are accessible to the child. When the scale of time becomes intelligible, for him past events acquire an exact "address"—a when. A "grid" of time is reflected in memory in the form of models of words and numbers, and past events are associated with some of them. Models from temporary memory move into permanent memory either in the form of separate or distinct bright pictures or in the form of meaning models at higher levels. For example, for future pupils the concept "the great patriotic war" is a very general model which is associated with the years 1941 to 1945. For participants in this war, this is, in addition, distinct events divided into years, months, and for some, into days and even into hours. Consequently, in the memory, models are stored at various meaning levels each possessing connections (addresses) with models of time which are exact or approximate. In recalling events, it is possible to establish a time of their occurrence by means of these connections. Even the inverse activity is possible—when events are established according to the "network of time" in which they took place. A diagram of such a network and of models connected with it is depicted in Fig. 35.

Attention to the past is a program of recollections. In order to recall an event, it is necessary to excite the model of this event from permanent memory to that point where it will be able to "win over" attention.   This will occur only if a quantity of energy will be moved along associated connections to a corresponding model of sufficient strength to raise its potential (activity) to the level at which the model will be able to compete successfully with other models.   For this to occur a source of energy is required—an excited model and its connections with the unknown.   These connections need not be direct; in fact, they may pass through an entire circuit of some other models. The "ease" of recollection is determined by the penetrability (by the resistance) of connections, "by the power of the energy source"—by the level of activity of the model and by the threshold of excitability of the desired model.

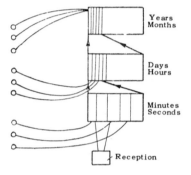

FIG. 35. Schematic of the "network of time" and of the models-images associated with them.

This "ease" is the time necessary for recollection. This time is consumed in the penetration of little used connections in intermediate links or in the excitation of different collateral phenomena which have a connection with the necessary model (we recall "A Horse-Named Family" by Chekov). Repetitive changes of the threshold of excitability (spontaneous activity) are significant both for intermediate models and for final models. The process of recall can be delayed by the model connections with other models. The schematic of a program of recall is shown in Fig. 36.

I is a model of the source of search; a, b, and c are models-qualities from higher or auxiliary codes. Initially, a is activated across connection 1, from here the search is directed across connection 2 to the required model X. If this is insufficient, model b is switched-in and then model c is introduced, with their respective connections 4 and 6. When the concentrated activity from all three points becomes sufficient to raise the level of activity of X, this model will "win" attention and will move into consciousness, that is, it will be recalled. Verification follows this, that is, excitation across connections 7 and 8 of new models-qualities d and g, from which the connections 9 and 10 return to the initial model.

Turning to memory—the activation of a program of recall arises from various sources:

1. From a direct order or question. Usually, the order or question indicates models-qualities necessary for the required identification.

2. From the overall program of investigation of any system. Such a program undoubtedly exists and consists of several sub-programs which are activated in sequence from the central model. Such a system may include structure, history, qualities, function, and so forth.

3. From any model from the present or from the past which is sufficiently strong to seize attention.

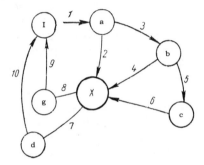

FIG. 36. Schematic of the program of recall.

A model-image "which has been recalled" for any reason is transformed, as it were, into a perceived model and in this may be subjected to a new distribution of levels with the generation of different primary and supplementary codes-qualities, which may not have been discovered in the initial perception of the object in that this processing offers a different direction of analysis than that which was originally selected. Thus a person having recalled a past event and having thought about it anew may find in this event previously unnoticed qualities.

The establishment of an event in long-term memory is determined less by the intensity of the excitation of its model at the moment of reception than by the number of subsequent repeated recollections. This is, in fact, the way the mechanism of memory works during one's entire life from the very first glance onward. One may begin the recall of an event from any level of its model— from the overall picture, from any particular detail, from any quality or meaning. Stimulation of one of these models may subsequently regenerate the remaining ones.

In connection with this, it is necessary to dwell on the possibility of transfer of excitation across levels of models not only "from below to above" as occurs with the hierarchical processing of information, but also "from above to below," that is, from models of meaning to models of images from which this meaning evolved. The conductivity of connections in various directions is probably not identical but it does exist.

Recall of the past is not simply a passive process of reestablishment of old connections and illumination of former images. It is far more complex than this. A man may correct his remembrance of the past. There are models-qualities of a higher level which reflect each past event. True images are recreated from them. If the connections are insufficient to permit specific recall of these models-qualities, images taken from other pictures may be substituted in that these are similar. Recollection is transformed into imagination, into creativity. This is done automatically, unconsciously, or intentionally (for example, as when a man is writing his memoirs he regenerates the conversation of his characters from the tone of the conversation which is preserved in his memory). Characteristically such "reconstructed" models of the past may subsequently remain in memory and may even completely replace the true pictures.

Foresight of the future is contained in the simplest motor programs. A model of the conjectured result of the activities is stored in a servosystem and the actual result is compared with it. This model is formulated on the basis of experience, that is, it is derived from the past.

Any program of suppositions or imagination is constructed according to this very same principle, but the program itself is detached from activities and exists independently. It is activated just as is the program of recall—by direct command or by means of a question from the general program of investigation of the system, and, finally, by means of chance excitation of the model.

In essence, imagination consists of the specification of the changes of the system in time when the initial state in which all its previous history is activated and the order of external influences expected in the future are given. In other words, the systems future state is calculated on the basis of its dynamic characteristics and inputs. Given this, various tasks become possible: such as, defining the state of a system with respect to time, following the changes of the system during this time interval both in the form of general tendency and specific functions. If there is already a system in the memory which exactly corresponds to the given one, imagination is reduced to the sequential recall of its changes in time—of independent changes, or of those changes which depend upon external influences. This variant completely corresponds to the program of foresight. Change of a system can be presented in any code: in the form of changing images, in the alteration of meanings of events, or, finally, in the dynamics of some one code-quality. Such a case is illustrated in Fig. 37.

The situation is quite different when there is no system similar to that one given in the memory and the system is specified in the form of higher-level models—by the enumeration of qualities and the meaning of events. According to these, it is necessary to reconstruct changes of the system and its state in models of a lower level, that is, in terms of sight and sound images, pictures, words. For this it is necessary to find separate images in the memory from other systems, images which satisfy the specified requirements. Something similar to this occurs in the selection of lower-level programs of activities which must satisfy various qualities of a higher level.

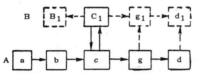

FIG. 37. Concept of the operation of dynamic recall developing through the analogy of systems. In memory the dynamics of system A is represented in the form of models a, b, c, g, d. For a similar system B there is a given state C_1. Then its future states g_1, d_1, are represented as a sequence of images of system A stored in memory.

Different variants for solution of a problem are possible within imagination:

1. There may be some meaning-models which determine the selection of a system and its program of changes.

2. A system may be given as an image at a lower level and it is necessary to follow its changes in time. Several variants of these changes are possible. From them one is selected at each point in time with the participation of inputs from the subconscious and frequently these are in the form of feelings.

3. A system is given as an image on a lower level and from it is selected several meaning codes-qualities—also with the participation of feelings. These meaning-models participate in the selection of a variant of subsequent transformations of the initial model of the image.

"Fantasy" and "imagination" are programs of the same type and can hardly be distinguished from one another.

As is well known, man can voluntarily activate a program of recall or imagination. To do this a model enters into his consciousness which designates a starting mechanism for a given program. It is formulated by words such as "remember," "imagine," or their equivalent on a higher level wherein the word itself is not pronounced. Such a model automatically activates the program from a beginning in which there are initial data—images on lower or on higher levels ("recall about something," "imagine what will happen in that event").

The next program characteristic of man is the will. The desire "I want," has general and particular expressions—"I want" something or "I don't want" something. These select and activate programs of activity and control their execution. Even noncortical animals possess a program which guarantees the completion of a motor act. A stimulus elicits a "feeling" which activates a program which, in turn, is executed up to its concluding stage. This triggers another "feeling" (of satisfaction?) thus making it possible for the next stimulus to activate another program. A program as a rule is executed up to its very end, but may be interrupted provided another stimulus more powerful than the preceding one begins to operate. This distinctive primitive will of animals can be explained in terms of the activity of a higher unconditioned reflex—a goal to which some feeling corresponds.

With the emergence of man, the completion of a main program has moved into the sphere of consciousness. Desire is realized, that is, it is associated with the words, "I want," and is activated as soon as its elicited program is completed. Immediately following this, the feeling which activates the given program disappears and is replaced by another feeling connected with the words, "I do not want." The realized desire—the excited cortical model "I want"—becomes a supplementary stimulus for the completion of a program. This is a simple variant of will. More generally, will may be described as the completion of one selected program despite disturbances generated by other external and internal stimuli. Initially only the model "I want" operates in the child. Subsequently, other models become manifest, such as, "must," "ashamed" (before people or of one's self), "conscience." The degree to which the stability of these cortical models has been inculcated by society is very important.

The following is a program for willful activity (its schematic being shown in Fig. 38):

1. The external or internal stimulus, E-IS.
2. This elicits the feeling F_1.
3. This feeling elicits the desire D_1.
4. There are several programs for the stimulus E-IS. Following their approximate evaluation in imagination, one is selected, P_1, this being dependent upon feeling and desire.
5. The selected program P_1 is minutely processed in the imagination and this elicits the final feeling F_2. If these then coincide in sign with the initial feeling F_1, they are amplified and the desire ("I want") is correspondingly amplified. When this desire reaches a determined magnitude, the decision R_1 is generated which activates the selective program of activity.
6. In the course of executing the program real difficulties arise. Real feeling F_3 are reactions to them. If F_3 correspond to the expected feelings, the program continues toward completion. In the event, however, of noncorrespondence (such as, fatigue),

it elicits the opposite desire, D_2 ("I do not want") with which a selection of another program P_2 is connected, as, for example, "to cease." This desire is worked over in the imagination and elicits the feeling F_4 which supports P_2.

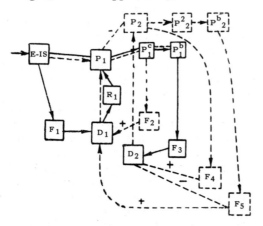

FIG. 38. Program of will. The dotted lines show the probabilistic connection of the models developed in imagination. Programs are realized by the unbroken lines--. The plus or minus signs associated with arrows indicate the amplification.

7. In the simplest case, if F_3 is opposite in sign to F_1 and is greater in magnitude, the program P_2 is activated and the execution of the first program ceases. This is just what occurs in animals and in children. The innate program of a reflection of a goal is a supplementary stabilizing factor demanding completion of the initiated activity. It suppresses the unpleasant feelings F_3.

8. The situation is much more complex in mature people. The very fact that there is a change of the program (a refusal) is taken into consideration during reprocessing of the program of cessation P_2, in the imagination as is its relation to cortical models of debt, conscience, shame, and so forth, P_2^a and P_2^b. As a result a new unpleasant feeling F_5, is generated (for example, shame). This feeling is compared with F_4, the assumed pleasant feelings which result from the cessation of the program P_2. If this proves to be more powerful, then P_2 (cessation) is not activated and the completion of the initial program P_1 is realized not only at the strength of the initial feelings (F_1 and F_2) but with the additional strength of the feelings of debt, shame, and conscience—F_5.

If these moral feelings (F_5) yield in intensity to feelings which elicit a desire to interrupt the program (F_3 and F_4), a new decision is adopted and the execution of the program ceases.

It would seem to me that "freedom of will" which is apparently distinctive to man is a fiction. Free decisions are but programs even though they may be highly complex and their intermediate stages may be concealed. These are frequently located in the subconscious and therefore manifest themselves in an apparently unrelated manner to other phenomena.

Thus, willful activities may be considered as a program of control of one's own behavior. At its input are located not only the concrete external and internal stimuli of the present but also other models, such as, duty, conscience, honor, which are inculcated by training and which are developed in the process of self-organization. These models belong to the highest level since some general qualities of different acts are reflected in them, short term and long term, which are expressed by different operations and words. In general, these models have connections of different stability with feelings. Their own activity is located on different levels. It is just this which determines the value of man as a member of some community of people. It is true that the process of one's own creativity—self-organization—rules of ethics which are inculcated by upbringing, can be subjected to significant changes up to their complete denial. The complex of models of moral ethical characteristic distinguishes man from the other animals and represents still another servosystem by which all phenomena perceived by the individual and the individual's actions find reflection. This is the system which attempts to correct preceding errors.

Thus we already know of three mutually interacting systems-programs by which external and internal information is reprocessed and programs for the individual's activities are formulated:

1. a logical program inculcated by training;

2. a feeling program in which the instincts "for one's self" and "for the family" are reflected; and

3. a social program which reflects the ethics of the community.

It is characteristic that this last program operates through a second one—a feeling program. When the external world or the particular acts of an individual are analyzed (modeled) then models are reflected in all three programs. A logical program presupposes several possible responses and their selection is corrected according to the feelings elicited by the reflection of the stimulus in the "animal" and social program.

We can look at it this way: The external stimulus is subjected to analysis; information is generated from it which then goes through processing at various levels along with the production of main and supplementary codes-qualities. Processing is realized with the participation of a feelings sphere in the form of amplification of some models-standards which are utilized as the basis of comparison. Of course, even attention participates in this process and directs the process to that side associated with the more powerful feelings.

A variety of responses—of activities correspond to any model of an external stimulus at a particular level, this being due to the logical program imparted by training. It is necessary to select one of these. Selection is accomplished by means of the interaction of three components:

a. The extent to which the path from the model of the external stimulus to the activity is utilized, that is, the degree of memorization of the response as related to the stimulus according to a logical program of information processing.

b. Feeling amplification (through the elementary activity—desire) of one of the models of activities which is a function of the "animal" programs—instincts.

c. Feeling amplification of this model or of another model of activities from another source—from models of social ethics and morality which have been inculcated by upbringing. At the same time, each feeling can stimulate (excite) a program and suppress the remaining programs. As a result of this three-dimensional comparison, an individual variant is selected, amplified by attention, and activated. All other variants are temporarily suppressed.

This process can be depicted in another way. Receiving the stimulus we attempt to respond by a learned program of activities—this is a logical program. Then we introduce corrections as a function of the particular feelings—a program of emotion. Then once again we evaluate the possible response from the point of view of social norms (honor, conscience, good, and evil). This is a program of a second stage of social consciousness.

As has already been indicated, a third stage of consciousness is possible. We may think of this stage in an informational way as still a fourth reprocessing of information, a program having its own codes (qualities, levels) and connections with feelings. This program which develops as a result of the realization of the principle of self-amplification and the process of self-organization reflects the individuality of the person. A wide diversity of variants are possible at this stage, these ranging from pathological compulsion, fanaticism, to the highest manifestations of Yoga will, and of the intellect on the scholar or of the artist. Fundamentally, everything depends on which model or programs are amplified by the conditioning. We will dwell on some of these.

1. Servosystems of the higher level. These systems embrace the modeling of thoughts, that is, movements of processes of excitation according to cortical models, not only with the great activity characteristic of such movements and powerful emotions, but also for the insignificant activity which barely crosses the threshold of consciousness. At the second level of consciousness, man monitors his own activities, but on the third level, man follows his own thoughts, remembering these and subjecting them to analysis. Of course great memory and a slightly developed program of analysis is necessary in this regard.

2. A well-developed complex of will which can control both movements and thoughts. Will is generally understood as the undeviating completion of the specified program of activities despite

various external and internal disturbances. The control of thoughts is a higher stage since such control is associated with rapidly changing excitations of many models of little intensity. The principle of willful activities itself—the switching of excitation to a determined circle of previously designated models—remains the same. The difference here only lies in the level of difficulty. A servosystem is necessary for this program as is a very strong model of the concept "must" which characterizes the will and watches over the execution of the designated program. Attention keeps returning to the original models through this program.

3. A program of creativity in those areas of knowledge where generation of the highest forms of information and modeling of very complex systems is required. For example, such areas include philosophy, mathematics, psychology, and sociology.

4. A means for replacing the generally accepted norms of morality and ethics by newly created norms. These may be revolutionary and progressive and, in time, may win recognition or they may be antisocial, completely individualistic, even to the pathological extreme.

Yogists are examples of the third stage of consciousness. From their earliest age, devotees of Yoga go through very complex training. The basis of this training is concentration, that is, the development of mechanisms of an advanced servosystem and of models of "must." The training is reinforced by a corresponding regime of life, nutrition, and so forth. This subsequently provides a huge effect on the control of the organism, since it develops an undeviating will and permits cortical suppression or stimulation of different life functions, even those which are apparently not subject to consciousness. In all probability the potential of these conditioned models becomes so powerful as to penetrate many of the barriers between the cortex and other sections of the nervous system.

Reaching this third stage of consciousness does not necessarily endow man with great intelligence. A fakir or Yoga devotee may possess iron will but be unable to create anything useful. The intellect is a very different function. Probably the intellect should be defined as an accumulation in memory of a great quantity of models-facts and models-programs and of an ability to manipulate them. Of course a strong will and tenacity of purpose at this third stage of consciousness can significantly promote the development of intellect. But strength of will and tenacity of purpose can also result in deviations from social norms of behavior and, in fact, lead to extreme individualism. Man sometimes abuses his instruments of concentration and amplification, using these to deliberately amplify false models (ideas). This is why there are different religious, political, and even scientific fanatics. These fanatics are absolutely convinced of the validity of their position and exert a great influence on other people. It is possible that such extreme concentration on some cortical models can activate certain telepathic factors which are rarely displayed under ordinary circumstance.

In general, one cannot envision all variants of the third stage of consciousness since these develop in the sphere of self-organization.

Creativity and labor: Creativity is the most important program distinguishing man from the lower animals. It is true that this quality, as many others, is not simply a function of the brain but is, to a lesser degree, a consequence of the social influence on man.

Creativity consists of the creation of new models which were previously nonexistent or unknown to the given person.

In the final analysis, all systems are comprised of identical elements. The difference between systems is of a structural nature, that is, consists of a diversity of combination of elements and their distribution in space. The brain models systems external to us by means of nerve cells and their connections and by means of these very same elements, can create new models which will be transformed into other things with the availability of programs of conversion of cortical models, and, in turn, these may be embodied in physical models which influence the external world. Things—these are the very same objectively existing models as those which occur naturally.

Fantasy or imagination is an indispensable ingredient in programs of creativity. Here is the factor which creates new models in the cortex of the brain. A general algorithm for the program of imagination has already been indicated above. We shall now consider the entire order of creativity, including the transformation of cortical models into physical ones.

Creativity can begin at any level. As a rule the need for production arises externally, that is, a series of higher-level models dictate the basic qualities of the creativity which is required. For a machine, this might be its function. For a painting or a poem, it might be the thought or the idea, and for a scientific hypothesis, it might be its general principles.

Of course, ideas do not originate in a void. Rather they are the consequence of observation and analysis of phenomena of the external world, together with their feeling reflection. For the investigator, this is the question "What is this?"; for the designer, it concerns the imperfection of existing mechanisms.

The matter is far more complex for artists, since in the process of creativity, artists do not always begin from the highest level, that is, from ideas. Frequently, the first stage of creativity will arise from supplementary codes-qualities such as form, image, these originating in the imagination or perceived in the external world. Thus creativity begins "from the middle"—ideas are attached to fragments of a production—to partial models. This is especially true for lyrical productions such as poems, landscapes, and music.

Fantasy is the next point of the algorithm, the creation of a production in the imagination as an entirety, or in segments comprised of primary or secondary parts. In an informational way, this is a program for the selection of models-elements at lower levels according to the models-qualities of higher levels or, in other words, a program for the embodiment of ideas into concrete forms. The number of levels in the future model varies with the complexity of the model. Paintings which originate in the mind are immediately verified by other criteria; they are sensed, as it were, by an internal scan; information at various levels, having different supplementary codes-qualities, is generated from them and compared with the given models. The conversion of imagined forms into physical forms can be realized by various programs of activities—of read-out. The latter are also worked out initially in the imagination as "how to do it," "is it feasible?"

The execution of a program subsequently follows and is expressed in the form of a series of motor acts with the utilization of instruments and materials. This is labor. Its success depends upon the presence in the arsenal of memory of well-developed elementary movements from which motor acts are constructed in conformance to the general rules of the program of activities. Every completed part of an article is perceived via sense organs and analyzed as an external stimulus. The results are compared with those given—with those created in the imagination. Corresponding corrections which result from this comparison are introduced into future programs.

When the production is ready, it is once again subjected to perception and to analysis in its entirety, with the generation of higher codes-qualities and their comparison with those preliminary models which were established as the basis of the operation at its very inception. In addition to an evaluation of the labor, there may result ideas for the improvement and perfection of the production.

The whole process of creativity can be reduced to a search. Models-elements must be selected from lower levels which interact to produce qualities which are expressed as a series of given models at higher levels. This is a very complex and difficult process when one considers the probabilistic character of hierarchical recoding and the subjectivity of comparisons.

Man is trained to perform the simplest program of search—to find elements from within his memory having similar qualities to some particular one or answering to set conditions. For this there must be a realization of a program of recall. As has already been indicated, such a task is difficult if the conductivity of the connections with the associated models is poor or the model is suppressed. Frequently, time is required to break through to the given model. Often this occurs in the following way: A model is excited from a source completely unconnected with the initial task. The more general the form in which the idea for the production is expressed, the greater the number of possible variants for its completion, and possibly, the more varied the search.

The feeling sphere is the most important force and component of creativity. Feelings are primarily stimuli and consequently are sources of energy indispensible for search activity. We can designate several such stimuli:

1. Curiosity. This is the reflex "What is this?" It is a special feeling of anxiety which originates in information processing when the lack of a standard for comparison is discovered in the process of recognizing a model withdrawn from temporary memory. This feeling attracts attention-amplification which expends energy in a search—in an attempt to penetrate the poorly utilized paths with the goal of finding the required models in permanent memory.

2. The reflex of goal. Man (and even lower animals) obtains satisfaction in the execution of his work, of course this within specific limits up to the point of exhaustion or boredom. It is creative work which delivers the greatest satisfaction since this is less bound up with unpleasant consequences, and with fatigue resulting from monotony. Consequently, man engages in creative endeavors for the satisfaction he derives from them.

3. The reflex of self-expression: Satisfaction from activities in the monitoring of one's own thoughts and feelings.

4. Vanity is satisfaction derived from praise, this being equivalent to reenforcement of a conditioned reflex.

Each of these feelings is represented by specific innate models which can be amplified by training from without and by activity of the "principle of self-amplification." But in this case, the feeling itself becomes the stimulus for creativity. Most often a combination of feelings-stimuli occurs which is different for scholarly investigators, for artists, or for inventors. For the scientist, the primary force is curiosity. For the painter, the primary force is the satisfaction derived from creativity and self-expression. Of course, for all some amount of vanity can be added to these feelings.

Feelings take part in all stages of a creative program. They excite those higher models which provide ideas for things to be produced and impart subjectivity to the selection of models-elements on lower levels. The probabilistic comparison of an obtained model with the required one is accomplished on all levels with the participation of feelings which amplify some models-standards and weaken others. The results of the entire operation and its separate stages are evaluated in terms of satisfaction or disappointment.

It is very important that all the feeling accompaniment of the creative process be remembered with its content in order to serve as encouragement or constraint for subsequent endeavors of the same type. The extensive duration of feelings is a conditioning of their models and is converted into a stimulus. On the other hand, brevity in the duration of feelings becomes a suppressing factor.

The role of the response of people within the social environment is enormous, offering stimulation or suppression of vanity.

Labor is a necessary ingredient of creativity since only through labor can cortical models be converted into physical ones. This process is associated with fatigue and with disappointments when it is impossible to find physical expression for one's thoughts. Will-power is necessary for overcoming such unpleasant emotions. However, will is not always a sufficient condition for success. The process of converting an imagined model into a physical one may run into difficulties of reproduction, that is, the exact control of the motor sphere has limitations, these being extremely different for different people. Most probably these can be explained in terms of dissimilarity in degrees of conditioning or in terms of some innate peculiarities of the brain structure. Different people have different programs for the read-out of images from the analysis of sight and hearing. Evidently, with the help of early and persistent training, it is possible to significantly broaden the innate capabilities of the child. Upbringing will not create genius but in all probability a level of "talent" can be quite frequently attained. It is true that in the different cases, grossly different amounts of increased labor will be required.

Following this discussion of the basic programs of human behavior, the concept of "thinking" should not present any great difficulty nor should it require extensive explanation.

Thinking is a process of information reprocessing within the human brain. It is accomplished with close interrelation of various levels of the conscious and subconscious, this occurring according to general principles of hierarchical programming.

I have already mentioned the concept "thought." This is simply a cortical model to which attention is drawn at a given time, that model which demands the greatest potential in comparison with all others. This model can be related to different codes, levels, programs; it can reflect a perceived influence at any given moment or a recollection of previous activity.

It is wrong to identify a thought with words or phrases which are pronounced "to one's self." It is only necessary to observe one's self briefly to be convinced that we do not always think in terms of words. Frequently, an idea is an image, a sensation derived from one's activities or some model in terms of a higher level code—a concept, an abstraction which may subsequently be expressed in words but sometimes is never so expressed. Phrases which are mentally pronounced are incomplete and in the great majority of cases are reduced to simpler concepts.

As yet there is no way to determine the expenditure of time on any of these specific aspects of thinking. One can assume that our attention is frequently attracted by "suppressed" activities, this including the speech which occurs in terms of internally verbalized thoughts.

Primordial program exists in the cortex as is true of any informational system—"stimulus-activity." According to this program, every image of the external world has connections with models of some programs of activity. Most frequently there are models for the pronunciation of words which designate the name or property of the object under consideration. Therefore, having seen an object, we first recognize it and then automatically pronounce its name or designate its qualities mentally. Thought in terms of words is nothing more than suppressed speech. The ability to suppress movement is a consequence of upbringing. Small children chatter incessantly and cannot sit quietly in any one place. The ability to restrain one's movements comes only with time and with some difficulty.

A thought may be viewed as a real object which has been reflected in the cortex. That is, the activity of a model excited to reach the level of consciousness as a result of the influence of other models via its connections can be almost as great as the event of excitation of this model in the process of reception and recognition via a sense organ. In both cases the model is, so to speak, "illuminated" and moves from permanent memory to temporary memory where it can function as a source of excitation for other models which have well-utilized connections with it. In particular, one can separately identify hierarchical models and supplementary codes-qualities as in the case of sensing the external environment. In essence, programs of imagination are built upon this.

But man can nevertheless distinguish excitation of a model elicited by a real object from one that is imagined. It is possible that the difference between these is based on the level of activity, or this difference may be connected with the activity of servosystems which reflect the source of excitation—from sense organs or via association with other models. This is an important point because differences between the real and the imagined are erased in some diseases.

It is difficult to evaluate the quality of thinking or, in other words, the degree of optimality of human behavior. Criteria for evaluation must first be known and these may be contradictory in that they depend upon basic programs "for one's self," "for the family," "for society." Everything is determined by the "point of view." There is no need to overemphasize the purely informational aspects of the brain. This program for information reprocessing has at the very least three deficiencies.

1. Its finite limitation. In the brain, there may be an insufficient number of stored models-standards useful for comparison with models of the external world and little of the programs themselves for the generation of hierarchical meaning models. Consequently, it is not always possible to completely recognize phenomena and to subsequently respond to these. In addition, probabilistic recoding

causes error in recognition. Finally, the low speed of perception and analysis is a limiting factor.

2. Subjectivity.   As we have indicated more than once, the entire process of information reprocessing is accomplished with constant participation of the feeling sphere, this reflecting to a first approximation "animal" programs, that is, the particular interests of the individual at the given moment. Consequently, the participation of emotions can significantly distort information owing to a biased selection of models for comparison and estimation of results. Activity as an aspect of information reprocessing is even more subjective since the selection of models of muscular activity is directly determined by desires, that is, by derivatives of feelings. Errors resulting from the participation of feelings can be quite great and are, in general, proportional to the intensity of the feelings.   As an example, consider those crimes which occur in a state of emotion.

3. Obsession. Even with constant exercise, models of different stimuli can exert a real influence on the information reprocessing in the brain because of the "principles of self-amplification." This is accomplished through the feeling sphere: Stimuli excite feelings and the latter distort the program. The difference here lies in the fact that feelings are not excited from the subcortex, that is, from instincts, but on the contrary are excited from "above," that is, from the cortex. Nonetheless the result is the very same.

These three qualities of the brain distort our pictures of the external world. Cortical models only have relative correspondence to the real objects. The degree and direction of distortion is different in different people and is different at different times in the same person, this as a function of that person's emotional state and his degree of absorption in the activity.

From this one should not draw the conclusion that our ideas concerning the world are fundamentally incorrect. The distortions of perception are of various magnitude and sign (identical objects are frequently sensed under various emotional states), thus even the distortions of a single individual will be statistically averaged. As a result a more or less accurate model is created which may still suffer distortion under each subsequent perception provided, of course, that strong emotions are operating at the moment of perception.

Disturbances. People who suffer from mental illness differ from normal people in that their programs of behavior are deviant from the accepted norms and do not ensure the well-being of the individual in society.

Undoubtedly there is no fine line between mentally normal and mentally ill people. Quite a few so-called borderline states are known in psychiatry, states in which only a part of the programs of behavior are impaired, and sometimes this is only a very small part. Almost every man has experienced within his lifetime brief periods in which his behavior is borderline pathological, when he will respond to normal stimuli in an incongruous manner. The legal literature documents a multitude of such cases.

When they become distorted, any of the three above-described qualities of human programs may introduce a pathological state. Indeed, man may commit illogical or antisocial acts through ignorance, in a complex situation (a manifestation of the finite limitation), in a state of affectation, that is, under extreme emotional tension (subjectivity), or, finally, he may be so obsessed by his own ideas that his activities contradict the generally accepted norms.

And yet not all behavioral programs of the mentally ill are disturbed and thus distinguishable from accepted programs. Frequently, individuals who are mentally ill give an impression of normality and special investigations are required in order to disclose the insanity.

Consequently, each individual may be considered to be somewhat ''crazy''; he is considered to be mentally ill only when many of his programs are impaired over some period of time. It is important to note that the standards and limits of normality have materially changed in recent years and are continually changing as society develops.

All programs are structural. Some structures correspond to every human act and change of structure results in a new specific program. Developments within the field of psychiatry have vividly demonstrated this in that fewer and fewer mental illnesses still remain for which corresponding visible or microscopic changes in the brain have not been disclosed. Undoubtedly such changes are unavoidable in all diseases, but because of the molecular nature of some of these changes, they have not as yet become accessible to the investigator. Furthermore, in individual links, these changes may be quite insignificant but their composite effect may result in serious functional disturbances.

The structures of lower programs are stored from birth: These are neural reflex pathways for simple and complex instincts which occur both in the subcortex and the cortex. Here we find severely localized representations of different forms of sensitivity and for the control of different muscles.

Over this base level which performs the reprocessing of information by means of lower-order codes, there is superimposed higher levels of nerve cells having great numbers of interconnections. From this mass of connections which is manifest from birth offering poor conductivity for impulses, there develops well-utilized pathways through experience and training. Initially these connections may be of a chance nature but they are reinforced by repetition of function according to the principles of self-organization. Naturally, these structures are not rigid and can easily interact. It follows that cellular models are quite extensive in space and are not localized to a single point. In all probability, it is just this which explains the presence of the so-called mute zones of the cortex. Removal or injury of the cortex is not accompanied by visible functional disturbances of the nervous system or of the mind. The possibility cannot be overlooked that even now not all of the cortex is effectively utilized. Furthermore, basic centers of feelings are located in the subcortex. After removal of some cortical representation, a new center is more or less quickly created owing to the abundance of connections between cortex and subcortex.

In one way or another each cortical program has two structural forms: A structure which senses and analyzes (models) information and the model of the program which is related to it.

Programs can be subdivided into basic programs, that is, those which directly control the motor sphere and into supplementary programs, that is, those which impart different nuances, such as speed, force, and so forth.

"Breakage" may occur in any part of the model of the program: The changes of cells may be so significant or characteristic that the responses which strictly correspond to the responses of all other cells are altered.

As the biochemistry of the brain develops, there is increasing revelation of the delicate chemical specificity of cells of different parts of the brain and their functions. Evidently, this specificity is very great and as yet science knows little about it. With heterogeneous chemical influences, it is possible to cause the damaging of strictly isolated nervous cells, either in a single anatomical area or in several areas which may execute the same function.

One can imagine two causes for mental disturbance:

1. Primary injury to cells which ensure specific programs. These injuries are the result of external influences or disturbances of internal chemical regulation. They are accompanied by crude perceptible changes or molecular displacements which impair a specific function.

2. Functional hypertrophy of cortical cells as a result of their frequent and strong excitation, this resulting from application of the "principle of self-amplification." Evidently, innate peculiarities of cell programs can be promoted in this way.

Both of these mechanisms for cell disturbance can lead to mental illness provided they are localized in structures which relate to behavioral programs.

We are as yet far from the construction of hypotheses concerning the specific mechanisms of development of individual mental illnesses. I will therefore limit myself to several general remarks.

The following may lead to mental disturbances:

1. Change in the function of subjectivity; in other words, change of the "potential" of different departments of the feeling sphere. I have already mentioned that a man's mood is determined by the relationship of excitation of the universal "pleasure" and

"displeasure" centers.   Prevalence of the former leads to euphoria—to unjustified optimism, whereas a prevalence of the latter leads to depression—to pessimism. The emotions of joy and easily generated anger are extreme manifestations of the former. Fear is an extreme manifestation of the latter. Of course, change of emotions may lead to the selection of completely incongruous programs owing to incorrect analysis of the entering information and/or to the immediate selection of activities.

2. Impairment of mechanisms of consciousness and, in particular: a) the obliteration of the distinction between that which is real and that which is imagined (or conjectured or potential) with accompanying hallucinations; b) impairment of the model of "I" which can lead to reembodiment: to withdrawal, to dreams, or to fear.

3. "Amplification of feelings" and their pathological fixation. Some stimuli, combining at a single time with strong emotions, acquire a stable connection with these emotions. Upon repetition of the stimulus, the connection is increasingly reinforced. The entire complex if amplified becomes a "concealed" seat of excitation which attracts attention, and because of this, obtains still greater amplification. As a result there occurs hypertrophy of the model of the stimulus and feelings and full or partial distortion of the relations between models and the impairment of the adequacy of the responses. This mechanism explains all possible "manias" and "phobias" and also cases of pathological distortion of instincts and acquired responses (pathological thirst, sexuality, thievery).

4. The destruction of a large number of nervous cells leads to general mental deficiency insofar as degradation of all models in some measure sharply limits the possibilities of information reprocessing and memory.

In general, the matter may be summed up as a change of excitability of cortical models of feelings or programs which are damaged in diseases. "Sick" models can be localized at any level of the nervous system. Simple reflexes are destroyed when these models are located in the spinal cord or medulla oblongata, or higher in the brain stem. If they are localized in the cerebellum complex reflexes of equilibrium and coordination suffer. Damage to centers of the "old cortex" elicit sight and hearing disturbances and the impairment of movements. Pathological conditions still higher in the nervous system elicit the collapse of more complex nervous functions of information reprocessing, such as, reading, writing, and speech. Only damage of models located at the highest level lead to strictly mental disturbance such as destruction of the orientation with respect to time and space, relation of the individual to his social environment, the evaluation of complex information and operations, that is, those processes which are indispensible for the generation of higher levels of information and models. Fortunately, cases of isolated damage at very high levels are rather rare since the organism regenerates the norm with comparative ease.

5

Modeling of Mental Functions

A model is a system, a structure or a program of activity which in varying degree reflects another system, a structure, or a program. Modeling is a necessary condition for the generation of information. The brain of man, its cortex, represents a powerful modeling apparatus. The cortex creates its own models because of its diversity, first, because of the hierarchical structure of its nerve cells and, second, because of the structure of the molecules in the cells themselves. The change of energy within the cells—their activity expressed in the form of nerve impulses is still another means for the creation of models.

Types of cortical models. In the cortex one can arbitrarily identify two types of models:

1. Temporary models in which the external world is reflected for only a brief period of time. These represent complexes of excited nerve cells which reflect the object or the phenomenon. The excitation will die down and the model will disappear. Temporary memory exists on any level of the modeling system. It represents that portion of the information which has been transmitted from and in the code of the previous level to permit a comparison with models of symbols of a higher code which exist in the permanent memory. The duration of "glow" of a model of temporary memory is different for different levels. In a receptor cell, it is measured in instants, on the higher levels of meaning—possibly in minutes.

2. Permanent models or permanent memory are also represented by complexes of cells which reflect the external world, but they are interconnected by well-worn connections which offer various values of resistance. These connections may be innate or acquired.

Models of activities are programs stored in permanent memory in the very same way as other symbols. They function when their component cells are excited.

Temporary memory is connected with permanent memory through decrease in the resistance of connections and increase of the particular activity of cells as a result of frequent excitations of the models.

In all probability, the carriers of temporary and permanent memory in the cortex are one and the same cells. In that case temporary memory is represented by the excitation of a complex of cells, and permanent memory by connections between them. However, one cannot exclude the fact that cells—the carriers of temporary and permanent memory—are different, although they are connected in pairs (see Fig. 11).

Relationships between a system-object and the model. The most diverse relations between a system-object and the model are conceivable. In general, similarity between them is relative, being restricted only within certain limits. For example, as the graph shows in Fig. 39, the parameters of the object change from A to B, but the model repeats their change with accuracy of 95 percent only within the limits from A_1 to B_1. Outside of this segment there is no real coincidence.

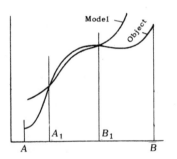

FIG. 39. The relation of characteristics of the object and of the model. They are close within the limits A_1 - B_1.

We can say the same thing about structure: A drawing of a model made from metal repeats some general features of the object, but this not more finely than some specific structural units. Even an exact copy does not reflect the molecular structure of the original. Precision and the limits of modeling can be expressed mathematically. To do this it is necessary to build another very precise model of the object and compare it with the original one. For example, here is an engine and there is its physical model. One can record the characteristics of each of these, that is, obtain a mathematical or graphical model with respect to some single function and then compare them.

A complex system has many programs. They are all connected, but these connections are not quantitatively identical. Some programs are inseparable from one another, are executed simultaneously and constantly interact, others exist more or less independently or, in general, are mutually exclusive. These relationships concern both neighboring programs and those situated at different levels. Physiology offers many such examples. The activity of the heart is closely connected with the regulation of the blood vessels, but its connection with the digestive tract is far less: with a full stomach, the momentary volume of the heart is only 5 percent less than with an empty stomach.

Modeling of complex systems will always be probabilistic since it is impossible to reproduce all programs of a complex object in the model. It is necessary to model selectively, artificially breaking off selected programs from the neighboring ones or beginning the modeling at some level, ignoring all lower levels. For example, we model programs of the heart as an entire isolated organ in the form of dependencies of its productivity in the flow of blood in view of the back-pressure in the aorta. Moreover, here we disregard the "cellular" and all lower levels, as well as the regulating influences of the nervous and endocrine systems. As a result the model will yield satisfactory coincidence with the original only within narrowly specified conditions—under specific regimes of life and of stress, this as a function of the significance of other programs which we have ignored.

In general, in building a model it is always necessary to have an idea of the limits of its applicability and of its degree of coincidence with the original. Modeling is competent only when the error (the noncoincidence) is expressed by a number close to the accuracy of measurement of the corresponding parameter.

All of this appears convincing while considering the modeling of relatively simple systems which have few inputs and where the change of the outputs fall within strict limits. In the modeling of human behavior, it is quite difficult to quantitatively evaluate the degree of coincidence of the model and of the original. For this it would be necessary to have quantitative expression for all information with its numerous hierarchical codes reflecting the diversity of qualities. As already mentioned in the first chapter, it is exceedingly difficult to solve such a problem, although in principle it is possible to solve this problem with the condition that the comparison of the model and the original will be done relative to some third system. Since there is no other alternative, only general methods of modeling and criteria for their evaluation must be applied to man.

Types of physical models. Man, long ago, learned to express his cortical models by physical means. Drawings are a most ancient code. We utilize them to this day, not only in art but in science as well (plans, schematics). They reflect structure and sometimes, within certain tolerance, function—as an alteration of structure in time. Quantitative coincidence is attained through use of a scale.

Verbal descriptions are the next most ancient code. As a rule, models composed of words have a qualitative character; numbers associated with them impart some quantitative significance. Similar models can be employed for cognitive aims, but these are unsuitable for substitution of the original or for accurate control of a system.

Mathematical models have a quantitative character. Two basic methods are employed: numerical and analytical. The first embraces coding of inputs and outputs by numbers, their interrelation being expressed by tables (see below). The second method embraces the expression of relations between inputs and outputs in the form of formulas—of algebraic or differential equations. This method is more precise since it allows calculation of the outputs for any states of the inputs, and not just for those which are determined by the concrete collection of numbers specified in the table. This method is, however, more difficult since it is possible to obtain analytical dependencies only for relatively simple systems with a small number of inputs and outputs.

Any mathematical model, as long as it remains on paper in the form of formulas and numbers cannot emerge as an independent system. Only a physical model can do this, a model which has a material structure and is capable of functioning and exerting influence on surrounding objects, that is, of communicating energy to them. For simple cases this is a machine created according to sketches, calculations, and descriptions. For reproduction of complex programs—this is an electronic modeling apparatus combined with output mechanisms which are capable of controlling machines or even people. Creation of such models requires the corresponding technology and materials. This condition, in significant measure, limits the realization of mathematical models. Exceedingly complex machines simply do not operate because of imperfection of their elements on that lower level which is necessary for any system—natural or artificial.

We will dwell in some greater detail on the basic approaches to modeling and on the types of mathematical models. Two different approaches are possible:

1. A system is represented as a "black box," that is, examined only from the point of view of its inputs and outputs, disregarding its internal structure completely.

2. A system can be considered as a complex structure which is composed of specific subdivisions and elements which are united by connections. The inputs do not operate on the entire system, but only on specific parts of the system, hence the outputs are a result of the interaction of concrete elements and subsystems. Such an approach, we will arbitrarily call "structural analysis."

In turn, two types of mathematical models are also possible: a collection of numbers or formulas as distinct from differential or algebraic equations. This concerns modeling of either a "black box" or of a structure. Knowing the characteristics of the elements and of the connections, it is possible to "check" the latter according to all of their components. A characteristic is the relation between input and output for a given element or a connection. This can be expressed by a collection of numbers or by formulas. Calculation is reduced to the synthesis of a complex mathematical model.

The interrelationship of methods is expressed in the following table.

"Black Box"	Numerical model Analytical model	Physical models
Structure	Numerical calculation Analytical calculation	

In essence the difference between all four variants can be reduced to the method of construction of the characteristic. In the
case of the "black box" the characteristic is obtained for the
system as an entirety, with the structural approach it is computed
from the partial characteristics of elements and connections.

A characteristic is a mathematical model of a program of information processing—of an entire system or of some part of it.
The characteristic itself is expressed by numbers or by formulas.

Systems can be subdivided into two basic types: noninertial and
inertial; they operate in a static or dynamic regime. Noninertial
systems do not possess "memory"—a change in the input is
immediately responded to by a change in the output. Thus, for
each state of the input there corresponds a single determined state
of the output. The characteristic of such a system can be expressed
analytically by a system of algebraic equations from which it is
possible to construct a single-valued continuous curve which relates the input to output values. A second expression—numerical,
takes the form of a table, in which inputs and outputs are shown as
discrete magnitudes and are coded by numbers. For each number
at the input there is a corresponding specific number at the output.
Such a characteristic of a system is called static.

Let us consider an example. Suppose that there is a system
with a single input and a single output (its functional schematic is
shown in Fig. 40). We will designate the input by x, the output
by y. Thus, the analytic dependency between these is expressed
by the formula $y = f(x)$. Here f designates the functional dependency
of y on x. It can be expressed by a permanent coefficient, by some
degree, or by any more complex formula. However, in all cases
it is possible to depict it by a curve on a plane. For expression
of a characteristic by numbers it is necessary to lay out the whole
range of changes of input and output magnitudes in "steps," intervals, and to record these by numbers; either absolute or relative—
by a code. For example, as the value at the input is changed from
0 to 100, the output changes from 20 to 200. The size of the steps
is selected as a function of the accuracy of the measurement or of
the convenience of calculation. Let us assume, for example, that
the input is 10 for an output of 25. Then we can record the characteristic as follows:

$$
\begin{array}{rcl}
0 & - & 20 \\
10 & - & 20 \\
30 & - & 50 \\
\cdot\;\cdot & \cdot & \cdot\;\cdot \\
100 & - & 200
\end{array}
$$

We will call each step a "letter." Then the possible alphabet
at the input will consist of ten letters and the output of eight.
For every letter of the input there is its corresponding output
letter.

Of course, the accuracy of such a characteristic is relative, since if the number 16 is the input, we must "round" it to 20 in order to adjust to the nearest letter. The same applies to the output. The fewer the steps, the less precise the characteristic.

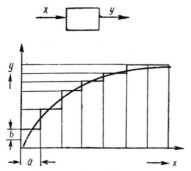

FIG. 40. A graph which shows the substitution of a continuous function by a discrete one (units of measurement: for $x - a$, for $y - b$). The smooth curve is transformed into a stepped one with inescapable distortion.

In our example, we could have taken gradations of 40 and of 50, then the accuracy would have decreased by half, but, on the other hand, the number of letters in the alphabet would also have been divided by two. Consequently, the calculation would have become simpler.

To obtain a mathematical expression of the characteristic of a system, it is necessary to test it, measuring inputs and outputs. Having obtained collections of numbers, it is possible to construct a formula for the dependency according to them or, having selected a value of step size and round-off, compile a table of correspondence between inputs and outputs. Moreover, without fail we must consider the accuracy of the measurements. If the system is really non-inertial, then upon repetition after some interval of time, for any value at the input we must obtain the same corresponding value at the output, these differing from one another only in the magnitude of the possible error of the measurement. If this is not the case either the system has inertia or there are some factors at the input which we did not take into account.

Let us imagine a more complex system with three inputs and three outputs. For each output we can write two equations:

$$y = f(m, n, p); \quad z = \psi(m, n, p).$$

Graphically, each function will represent lines in three-dimensional space. It is possible to approximately depict these on a plane in the form of a family of curves (Fig. 41). To express the system in number calculus, it is necessary to determine limits over which the inputs and outputs may change, then divide these into steps and code each step by a specific number or letter. Thus we obtain three alphabets at the input and two at the output. For example:

$$m_1 \ m_2 \ m_3$$
$$n_1 \ n_2 \ n_3 \ n_4$$
$$p_1 \ p_2 \ p_3$$
$$y_1 \ y_2 \ y_3$$
$$z_1 \ z_2 \ z_3 \ z_4$$

From a combination of these particular inputs it is possible to obtain many combinations, of which only a few are encountered.

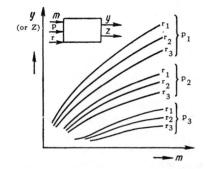

FIG. 41. Graphical expression of the dependencies with several inputs. The curves are constructed only for specific values.

We will replace the different combinations of letters at the input by a new alphabet, designating these by other letters. For example, let

$$m_1 n_1 p_1 = A$$
$$m_2 n_2 p_2 = B$$
$$y_2 z_1 = K$$
$$y_3 z_1 = L$$
$$\cdots \cdots$$

$ABKL$ are members of an alphabet which describes a second level of dependency between the letters of the first level,

$$A\text{-}K$$
$$B\text{-}L\,.$$

Thus it is possible to rewrite the whole system in terms of a new generalized alphabet, as is shown in the example. Naturally, letters are replaced by numbers. Of course, with a significant quantity of separate inputs and many gradations of each, the number of possible combinations which can be obtained will be very great, but in the process of experience with a system it often turns out that only a part of them is encountered. The remainder are not employed and thus do not appear in the table. This method in itself has become possible only with the appearance of digital computers which are capable of sorting rapidly through numbers.

The system shown above includes the possibility of generating several levels of alphabets-codes for inputs and outputs. A "memoryless automaton" works according to such a principle. For an influence at the input there is single-valued response at the output—no matter how complex it may be. Preceding changes of the input have no significance.

All living systems operate according to another principle: they are reorganized in the process of reacting to stimuli, that is, they have a memory in which past "questions" and "answers" are partially imprinted.

Applied to the simplest system with one input and one output, analytical dependency between them will be expressed not by the algebraic equation $y = f(x)$, but by a differential equation, in which the value of the output depends not only on the absolute magnitude of the input, but also on the rapidity of its change during some preceding interval of time. There can be even more complex dependencies, as, for example, on the acceleration of the input.

In a complex system with several (or many) inputs and outputs, analytical dependencies are expressed by very complex systems of differential equations, which are difficult to establish and still more difficult to solve.

A numerical method is more suitable for the modeling of complex systems. Introducing steps, the discrete expression of values, we, to a greater or lesser degree, increase the crudeness of the dependencies and, by doing this, decrease the volume of information.

In a "memoryless" automaton we are concerned with letters of alphabets at different levels, in an "automaton with memory" we are concerned with "words," composed of letters. These words designate, first, that an instantaneous response depends not only on the state of the input at a given moment, but also on the inputs during previous segments of time. Second, changes at the output are not limited to momentary values, but may be continued for still some time. A table of correspondence of words might appear as follows:

```
Time:     1 2 3        4 5 6
          Inputs:      Outputs:
          A B B ───→ O K L
          B A A ───→ K M N
          ─────        ─────
          Word         Word
```

In the given case it is assumed that a new complex of stimuli which change in time arrives at the system only after it has given a full answer and comes to some neutral original state. This is as if in a conversation between two people, a question was initially asked, then a response was pronounced, this being followed by the usual cycle: question—answer. In reality, the situation is more complex: there remains a certain "consequence" both after previous questions and also of particular answers. This corresponds to a significant lengthening of the memory with quite different significance for the first and last letters in the word.

The type of selected model and method of modeling—"structural analysis" or "black box," a numerical or analytical model—depends on the peculiarities of the modeling system, purposes of the model and availability of technological means.

Let us turn to the modeling of the mind.

The brain is a very complex modeling system. It processes a vast amount of information, obtaining this in the form of different physical influences in which are stored more or less hierarchical models of meaning. The basic means for the output of information—muscle movements are also extremely varied and bear a different informational load. In general, this is a system of hierarchical information processing having many diverse levels.

The structure of the system is known only in general outline. Not only are the higher levels of the cortex unclear but so are the lower ones—the receptors and muscle endings, the spinal cord and medulla oblongata, the subcortex, not to mention the delicate molecular structure of cells. Considering this, modeling per se must begin from an intermediate state, for example, from certain images at the input and with simple complexes of movements at the output.

The purpose of a brain model can be quite diverse. As yet, it is impossible to imagine all aspects of its future utilization. Let me list a few:

1. The creation of technological mechanisms which in varying degree can replace man. These may be robots suitable for hard physical labor and the control of other machines, but machines intended for the control of people, for example, in the sphere of economics, are also fully conceivable.

2. Heuristic models for the investigation of hypotheses concerning programs of the mind. These include programs with the aim of studying mechanisms of mental disorder in the search for methods for their treatment.

3. Models of man as an element of a social system intended for their heuristic modeling.

The technological means presently at the disposal of science are still far below the complexity of elements of living systems, although it is true that they possess some advantages, for example, they have great speed in information processing. In general, we program universal digital computers only within the possibilities offered by their specialized mechanisms. They satisfactorily permit us to create large models according to the type of digital computer. Analog machines are of lesser significance, however, there are possibilities for combining them with digital machines.

Finally, there exist special means for modeling, for example, the learning matrix, which are only now being investigated.

For technological mechanisms, the most suitable schematic of a model is the "black box." Based on the general laws of information processing in the organism, scientists and engineers will create a "new man," not at all confined to the preprogrammed schematics of the original. Any complex program can be reproduced in many ways—according to different schematics. The selection of some one of these depends on the means at the disposal of the designers. Although the human organism as an informational system is quite efficient, it is certainly possible to create much more efficient systems.

Modeling with the aim of understanding the laws of the activity of the organism is another matter. Here it is essential to adhere to the structural method, because it can throw light on the interaction of parts of the organism. Unfortunately, artificial technological means restrict the possibilities for reproduction of the natural structure, and even our knowledge about this structure is insufficient. Briefly stated, we do not have an artificial neuron and know too little about how real neurons are associated with each other in the nervous system. Therefore, modeling must begin from "coarse blocks"—hypothetical models of cells so as to elucidate the relations between them. Of course, such a model has only a relative similarity with the original, but this can be of some use. The basis for this opinion rests upon situations which concern some mutual-dependency of programs in the organism—both neighboring and hierarchical.

Selection of a method of modeling—of a numerical or analytical method—is determined by the available means and the complexity of the system. Evidently, one has to restrict himself to the discrete method or utilize the analytical method only in part since digital machines remain the basic modeling apparatus. The point is that millions, if not billions of large and small programs are executed simultaneously in the brain whereas in electronic computers, it is necessary to "stretch" them into one or several chains. Of course, with parallel processing it is difficult to speak of high precision of modeling. However, undoubtedly, the future belongs to special installations which, in principle, approximate the activities of the nervous network.

To imagine the volume of work in modeling, we will begin with an enumeration of the basic programs (that is, of the algorithms) which are inherent to man as a system for processing information.

The "law of connections" and the "law of energy" lies at the base of all models. The first reflects permanent memory and structure, the second relates to temporary memory and function. It is equally important to model these by the "black box" and by the structural technique.

The law of connections reflects the dependence of the resistance of a connection (the degree to which it is well-worn) on its use. This dependence is complex and nonlinear. In the physiological aspect, its components are numbers of impulses which pass through a synapse in a unit of time, in an informational aspect—the relative significance of "active" time of functioning of the connection and the degree of its activity, in other words, the quantity of energy conducted per unit of time. If the connection is not employed for some time, then forgetting occurs, although not completely. It is possible that having achieved a certain level of stability, the connections are not forgotten.

Of course, the coefficients of connection and their characteristics vary for different sections of the cortex. It is even difficult for me to produce an hypothetical curve for the resistance of the connection, however, one can indirectly derive it from an experimental investigation of memory. It is possible that the characteristics could have a form as shown in Fig. 42.

The law of energy reflects how the activity of a cell depends on the stimuli eliciting the activity. The basic parameters of activity are intensity (frequency) and the duration of impulsing after a single stimulation. This characteristic is not invariant. In all probability, upon systematic excitation of a cell there is a change, whereupon there are two possibilities: hypertrophy wherein the particular activity of the cell in response to identical stimuli from without is increased, and adaptation wherein the activity is lowered

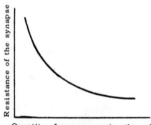

Quantity of energy passing through the synapse for some time

FIG. 42. Dependency of resistance of the synapse on the quantity of energy passing through it.

or completely disappears (Fig. 43). It is important to distinguish inhibiting influences which to a first approximation can be considered as activity with an inverse sign, but it is possible that the dependency is far more complex (see Fig. 45).

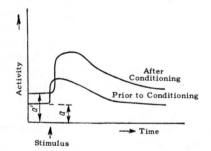

FIG. 43. Dynamic characteristics of the neuron prior to and following conditioning. a — spontaneous activity at rest.

Both of these laws relate equally to separate nerve cells and to entire groups of nerve cells, that is, to cortical models of different complexity.   It is essential to keep this in mind when modeling.

It is particularly important to consider the spontaneous activity of cells and models which depends on their level and on their conditioning.

List of mental programs.

1. Hierarchical information processing:

    a) recognition with the generation of main hierarchical, supplementary, and miscellaneous codes-qualities;

    b) probabilistic and not identical recoding (comparison);

    c) the changing of permanent memory as a function of exercise;

    d) a program for the formation of new higher levels due to training or self-organization;

    e) a program for the formation of different associations between models within the limits of a single level, between levels, and between different cortical analyzers.

2. Motor programs:

    a) the hierarchical construction of programs of movements;

    b) flexibility: for each model of a higher level there must be several variants of models of lower levels, probabilistic correspondence between them, selection of a model of a lower level from the several variants is determined not only by the state of the "periphery," but also by the combined activity of several models of upper levels, which reflect qualities;

    c) the presence on each level of servosystems in which a "copy" of the programs is imprinted and connected with systems of feedback: from executive organs; from muscles and joints; from the object of the influence; from the feeling sphere;

    d) foresight of the results: when a program is activated, a model of the expected results is simultaneously activated. This concerns all levels—in the form of general and partial programs.   Foresight is closely related to servosystems which note the degree of coincidence, conjectured and real. If disagreement develops, supplementary programs are then switched-in which amplify or correct the given program and sometimes disengage it as an erroneous program.

    e) memorization of the results and correction of the initial model of the program according to them. This concerns all three servosystems—results of the execution of the program are fixed in them in the form of a temporary model. Upon coincidence of the temporary model with the original one, the servosystems reinforce the latter and upon deviation apply a correction to it. Thus, the program continually approaches an optimum;

f) search and improvement. With a new stimulus for which a program of activities has not yet been developed, a system of programs of search is activated. These are separate standard activities, the results of which are fixed by feedbacks; and by these an optimum program is formed. The main role in the execution of the latter is played by the feeling sphere—satisfaction with success and discontent with errors;

g) computation from the feeling image—due to the reflex of imitation.   This concerns the reproduction of audible sounds and the coding of movements of visual forms (as in drawing).

3. Programs of feelings (models of feelings, associated with instincts and complex reflexes—imitation, orientation, freedom, goal, and so forth are included here):

a) a type model of feeling, simple and complex feelings, combinations of feelings;

b) models of instincts, their subcortical and cortical components;

c) models of emotions (in connection with instincts, reflexes and cortical models);

d) subjectivity of information processing;

e) "desire" and subjectivity of motor programs;

f) models of programs of complex reflexes: of orientation, imitation, goal, freedom, self-expression;

g) interaction of feeling and logical programs of information processing;

h) general model of the feeling sphere.

4. Programs of speech:

a) general principle of the possibility of information processing according to parallel programs;

b) the organizing role of speech in the formation of higher levels of information processing.

5. Programs of consciousness and subconsciousness:

a) the first degree of consciousness is a program of attention, processing of information arriving along several channels of connection, the system of amplification and inhibition, its characteristics;

b) the second degree of consciousness is the model of one's own "I," special servosystem which reflects and models its own sensations and the activities of other persons.

c) models of time: present, past, future, the program of imagination, the program of recall, the voluntary switching-over from one to the other, real and imagined;

d) programs of the will;

e) a third degree of consciousness are models of one's own thoughts.

6. Programs of creativity and labor:
   a) a general program of the formation of new models in the cortex of the brain and its components: systematic search of models-elements on lower levels according to several models of upper levels; random search; verification of a model according to other higher codes-qualities with feeling accompaniment;
   b) program of labor—the translation of cortical programs into physical ones and their subsequent improvement.
7. Modeling of the "principle of self-amplification" and of "enthusiasm" as qualities of the human mind.
8. Modeling of the flow of thought.

This list testifies to the fact that human behavior—man's mind and activity—is composed of a great number of interacting programs and models. Of course, they are strictly individual. The differences between people is explained by hereditary factors—by anatomical and functional peculiarities of the separate areas of the cortex and of the lower regulating systems. Then there are factors of upbringing and education—methods and tempos of filling the cortex with various models (facts, concepts, programs, information processing, the formation of feelings), and their quantity. A third factor operates in parallel—one's own particular creativity which concerns not only the creation of new models—of real things, but of programs of behavior as well. It is difficult to say which of these factors has primary significance. It seems to me that for the majority of people training is paramount, as is creativity. Without upbringing man remains an animal. However, one cannot dismiss his innate endowment. With proper training, it permits some people to reach exceptional heights which are completely unattainable for the majority of people. Questions of scientific upbringing still await the investigator. A necessary condition for success will be the improvement in methods for the investigation of the personality which will permit exploitation of the individual peculiarities of each person and to control the process of training.

Modeling of the mind. This can be reduced to the creation of automata which possess features of man. Their complexity and peculiarities will depend on the collection of programs which are stored in them. In connection with this, it seems expedient to note certain types, or classes, of "thinking" machines and to enumerate the basic programs which characterize each of these:

1. Model "Automaton." It is characterized by programs for the sensing of information with hierarchical processing of these data and multilevel programs of activities having almost all of the above enumerated components. With a diversity of inputs, it is possible that the program of selection will require use of a most powerful stimulus-amplifying system—attention. The automaton can learn. Elements of self-organization can be imparted to it,

that is, of the search for the optimum variant useful for the re-building of its structure. There are quantitative differences between the volume of information processing and the number of components in separate programs. The main peculiarity of this class of machines is that a single "logical" program of behavior underlies their activity, such program varying only moderately with training and development.

2. Model "Animal." In contrast to the preceding model, it possesses a parallel "feeling" program of information processing in which "interests" of the machine are reflected as independent units. It has a program for the processing of external information (as was true of the preceding system), but in addition it has its own "instincts" which introduce corrections, "subjectivity" in both sensing and activity. Such a machine is adapted for existence in the face of previously unforeseen conditions. Programs for learning and improvement in this model can be expressed in various degrees, possibly, even to a lesser degree than in that of a "pure" automaton.

3. Model "Man." It is distinguished from models "Animal" and "automaton" by the presence of a second step of consciousness—by models of "I" and of time, by programs of imagination, recollection, will, labor, and creativity. Of course, in this class of models many different variants may occur—according to the volume of information processed, according to the quantity and level of the higher models of personality which have emerged as a result of self-organization and the utilization of the "principle of self-amplification."

The creation of the model "Man" is not the ultimate limit. Even if it is impossible to increase the brain of man, the possibilities for broadening his technological systems are limitless. Therefore, the creation of a model "Superman" is conceivable as a result of the collective labor of people. It is now difficult to predict its programs, since it will surpass us in intellect. We can only assume that this "machine" will possess, first of all, quantitative distinction—a huge volume of information processing and the capability to generate higher codes-qualities. The meaning of very complex events which escape the individual man will become accessible to it. Its feeling sphere, possibly, will in itself embody models of many personalities—of an entire society. However, these programs are unclear for the time being.

It is necessary to clearly understand that, having created "Man," its authors will to a significant degree lose power over it and will not be able to accurately envision the direction of development of its personality. "His" programs of self-organization will yield only to limited influences, and the "principle of self-amplification" might make a madman out of him; it might hypertrophy any defect. Therefore, it is important to be very attentive to the modeling of its basic programs and to provide some distinct type of "arresting device." The question concerning control of "Super-man" simply loses meaning, since its basic features of personality will be formed independently, resting on a "data base" far more extensive than that of a single man. Therefore the creation of such systems can prove dangerous even in the event where they will not have been consigned the authority to control people.

The creation of thinking and feeling automata has already passed out of the sphere of the fantastic and has completely real foundations. This is a scientific problem, and its psychological and social aspects must be examined with all seriousness and responsibility. Machines which are too clever and independent can deliver misfortune greater than hydrogen bombs. And at the very same time, humanity cannot get along without them since the sharply increasing diversity of society can no longer be modeled by the human brain alone. Imperfection of modeling using the brain leads to loss of optimality in the control of society and this can lead to catastrophe since man has at his disposal such power-ful means of destruction as the hydrogen bomb. *

Let us return to concrete aspects of modeling of the mind.

As already mentioned, there are two principles of modeling:

1. First a system is studied in the process of testing or during its usual activity, and then a mathematical model is created accord-ing to the data obtained.

2. Heuristic modeling, is employed whenever it is not possible to obtain the necessary characteristics because of complexity of a system or because of the absence of methods for its investigation. Then the model is constructed on the basis of an hypothesis con-cerning the functioning of the system and a parallel test is con-ducted of the model and the original. Upon satisfactory coincidence, the model is considered to be successful, and the hypothesis on which it was based is considered to be reliable.

The brain is just such a system, a system which is impossible to comprehend at this time through use of classical analytical method. But, by observing the behavior of man, and by having certain data concerning the physiology of the central nervous sys-tem, it is possible to erect an hypothesis about the mechanisms of the mind in a general informational sense. Consequently, one must employ the method of heuristic models.

Technological means suitable for modeling take the form of computers—digital and analog, universal and special purpose. Furthermore, special physical models have been created which imitate the structure and the function of the brain by electronic means but, for the time being, these remain quite primitive. The point is that the structure of the brain has been studied inadequately and the technological elements from which it is necessary to re-create it hardly resemble nerve cells. Artificial neurons which

* The assumptions made above are controversial. (Editors.)

are now made in quantity in different countries of the world are so complex and cumbersome that it is possible to assemble only the simplest neuron networks from them. Yet it is true; in the future we will avail ourselves of just such synthetic networks having miniature and perfected elements.

The best contemporary computers possess very large external memory, but their working memory remains limited. Translation of data from one memory into another represents quite a slow process, therefore if the problem includes manipulation of a very great volume of data, the solution demands significant time. A second limiting factor is in the complexity of the construction and debugging of programs. As already mentioned, in the brain millions of programs are simultaneously operating at different levels, in the computer it is necessary to "stretch" them into one or several lines. This is very difficult and involves great expenditures of time.

Therefore the possibilities for the modeling of mental functions for the time being are limited by the comparatively small volume of stored information. It is possible to use this memory in two ways: either by creating complex models in which several (or even many) associated programs "work" but with only a small quantity of information, or to model separate programs, artificially separating them from others. In other words: to create a model of man with a small amount of data and programs in memory and operating within a narrow circle of conditions, or to select its mental function alone, but to "play it" on a large quantity of material. In all probability, it is necessary to proceed in both ways giving preference to either one of them as a function of the goals of the particular modeling—study of man or the creation of technological mechanisms which replace him.

The numerical methods employed in computers allow the modeling of a system as a "black box" or as a structure composed of separate elements. In essence the difference is that in the first case we create the structure anew, not claiming any similarity with the object and guiding ourselves only by the problem of reproduction of input-output relations, while in the second we are bound to an already prepared structure and we create a program for it. Structural modeling is much more complex since the quantity of connections between elements increases too many significant figures when there are a great number of them. Checking them must be done in sequence, periodically returning to an initial point along feedback connections, and all this is connected with a great expenditure of time and labor of programmers. It is just because of this that investigators occupied with nerve networks were compelled to limit themselves to several dozens of neurons. Of course, there can be no question but to begin modeling from nerve cells if the aim of the model is the mind and not physiology. In such a case the ultimate structural elements of systems subject to investigation on electronic computers must be models of images or of words. However, the structural method is more promising since it permits synthesis in one model of several programs and the simultaneous investigation of them. After the "checking" of programs of activity of a given system, it can be created in the form of a physical model, with of course the condition that elements having the necessary properties are successfully produced and an electronic computer is used to program them.

The general order of structural modeling can be reduced to the following points:

1. A structure is given comprised of nerve cells or of models. A number is given to each element.

2. Characteristics of the elements and the connections are assigned, this being expressed by a collection of numbers or formulas, originally as a static characteristic of the dependency of the particular activity of the cell (or model) on energy obtained from other models. The activity can be conditionally expressed as a "potential," and the obtained energy as a function of the "force of the current" and of the time of activity. An illustrative hypothetical graph of such a characteristic is shown in Fig. 44.

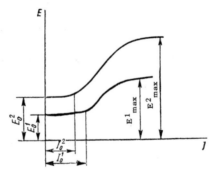

FIG. 44. Static characteristic of the neuron. E_0^1 – spontaneous activity, E_{max}^1 – maximum activity, I – quantity of energy obtained across the synapse per unit time, I_0^1 – threshold of excitability. The two curves — prior to and following conditioning.

With prolonged excitation of a model, its characteristic is changed due to hypertrophy. The particular activity of the model is also raised. In the graph the threshold of excitability and the height of spontaneous (particular) activity of the cell is shown.

Besides the positive energy received by means of the connections, there is negative energy—inhibition. This lowers the spontaneous and elicited activity of a cell according to a specific law (Fig. 45). It is possible that this dependency is linear.

The dynamic characteristic reflects the curve of change of activity in time after cessation of activity of the external (in relation to the model) stimuli. The duration of the action reflects the temporary memory of the model (see Fig. 43).

The characteristic of a connection is represented by its resistance, which can be conditionally compared to electrical resistance and expressed in some abstract units. All resistance appears at the synapse. The nerve conductor offers no obstruction for an impulse. Some initial value of the resistance exists from birth, this being different for different cells of the cortex. Subsequently, it changes as a function of some conditional value which one can express as the function of the difference of "potentials" (or of activity) on both ends of the connection and of time (see Fig. 42). This dependency is certainly quite complex and clearly nonlinear.

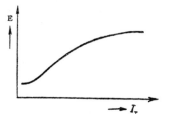

FIG. 45. Lowering of the activity of a cell as a result of inhibition. E_r - negative activity. I_r - its dependence on the energy of inhibition.

It is necessary to express the external influences on the system in those same conditional values of energy and of time as is the influence of some models on others.

The resistance of connections and the level of spontaneous activity of a model reflect permanent memory.

If we employ discrete numerical characteristics, a whole collection of them is required to express the activity of the model and the resistance of the connections.

In order to estimate the behavior of a system and its changes in time it is essential to specify the initial state of its elements and connections, then to break the time into brief intervals (units of time), and subsequently to calculate the change of activity of each element for the selected interval, the quantity of obtained and transmitted energy, depending on the activity of associated elements, and the resistance of their connection.

For example, for each element the following data are required which are reflected in memory:

1. Relative number of the element (cell, model).
2. General data concerning its activity:
    a) activity ("potential") towards the beginning of the period;
    b) the number of the static numerical characteristic of the spontaneous activity of the model—period and amplitude of its variations;
    c) the number of the static characteristic of the elicited activity. This characteristic shows the dependency of the activity on the energy of stimulation, obtained from the external environment (see Fig. 44);

d) the number of the related characteristic of the inhibiting influences on activity (see Fig. 45);

e) the number of the dynamic characteristic of the element—to a first approximation the law of change and duration of "reaction," that is, the extent of the activity after cessation of the action of the stimulus (see Fig. 43);

f) to this it would be possible to add the law according to which all characteristics are changed as a result of conditioning—of the systematic stimulation of the cell.

3. General facts concerning connections.

A. Connections from the given element to others, along which energy flows and for each:

a) the address—the number of the other cell;

b) the resistance at the beginning of the period;

c) the number describing the characteristic of the connection—the law of change of resistance as a function of the activity of both cells in time (see Fig. 42).

B. The same relative to the connections from other elements to the given one by which the latter receives energy.

C. The very same, but separately for inhibiting connections.

4. The characteristic of external influence—of the stimulus:

a) the address—of each element on which the stimulus operates;

b) the duration and intensity of its activity, expressed in conditional units of sensed energy (in the same units that are used to describe the energy transmitted from one element to another).

Then computation begins.   It is reduced to the following.

The quantity of positive energy received by each element during a time interval is calculated.   This calculation is also made with respect to the negative energy (inhibiting), both these calculations being based on the resistance and difference of potentials at the terminals of the connections.   Having obtained the increment of energy for a brief period and having the corresponding characteristics, it is possible to estimate the level of activity at the end of the period.

Calculation of the change of the resistance of the connections is in accordance with the selected characteristic, that is, it is determined by the quantity of energy transmitted by the connection. Then the resistance of the connections at the end of the time interval is calculated.

After this the whole computation is repeated for the following time interval.

Further, it is necessary to note the modeling of the temporal relay: the movement of excitation from one cell to another can occur without delay.   The mechanism of this phenomenon is simply the temporal summation of the arriving energy.   This may well be realized in particular cells which are capable of accumulating energy, subsequently increasing their activity in significant discrete amounts.

Such is the general type of computation of the behavior of a system which is performed according to its model. Behavior is a function of the structure, of the characteristics of the elements, and of the connections, as well as of the external influences. By changing these factors it is possible to obtain the most diverse variants of the programs of behavior.

At the output will be the amplitude of the activity of certain selected elements which execute a control function, for example, contract various muscles. However, if desired, it is possible to record the change of activity of any other elements of the system.

To go from this abstract schematic to a concrete model, it is necessary to assign all factors, a schematic, the characteristics, and the stimuli.

The creation of structural models of mental programs is a complex matter. It is necessary to devise schematics and specify characteristics of the elements. Unfortunately, physiology is at this time almost powerless to help. Evidently, it is necessary to begin with the modeling of elementary programs: hierarchical information processing, of hierarchical programs of activities, with models of the feeling sphere, and the interaction of feeling and logical programs. Then, too, it is possible to attempt to create models of elementary attention, the "principle of self-amplification" and, finally, of the simplest "flow of thought." The future will demonstrate the effect of such models. Undoubtedly, these are most closely related to the "true physiology."

A second approach to modeling of the mind represents realization of the "black box" method. Here it is necessary to create some automaton which processes information according to some programs which will result in the obtaining of specific dependencies between input and output which would correspond to the behavior of man. Moreover, the structure of the automaton and its programs are of little consequence.

The inputs to this system will be represented by numerous external influences in the form of flows of various energies which alter the intensity, spatial and temporal relations of its components. The outputs are the contraction of different muscles which may be combined in a variety of ways, changing in time and in intensity, or of course, their equivalents expressed as electrical impulses.

Between the inputs and outputs there are programs of information processing which are determined by hereditary factors (these being inputs) and training, that is, by the results of external influences (the inputs).

Hereditary information is transmitted in the form of the DNA of the embryonic cell, that is, it is in a molecular code. Programs for the realization of the future structure of the organism are stored in the genes. These are quite rigid complex programs resulting in the creation of a complex system capable of information processing having as goals the realization of basic programs "for one's self," "for the family," and "for the species." We have already spoken of this. Now, it is important for us to define in a purely informational way the essence of information processing by man in order to be able to construct an automaton which will replace him.

The diversity of the external world is infinitely great. Every automaton must encode it within certain frames—certain portions, such as quanta of time, space, forms of energy, their range of intensity, their relations, and so forth. In man the role of mechanisms which sense and quantify external influences belongs to receptors which convert these influences into nerve impulses. But only a small part of all possible influences are sensed. Consequently, even an automaton must have a mechanism which "selects" certain information from the total quantity of information. For this a system of transducers is necessary which sense and encode the external influence. Each transducer has its own alphabet—discrete states in which it can be found, and external influences corresponding to each of these. The receptors fall into various classes according to the forms of sensed energy— into sight, sound, tactile, and so forth. Receptors of a single kind are united by analyzers. For each analyzer there are many receptors; these states may also be varied. It is possible to replace a combination of these states by a new symbol in a higher alphabet so that the diversity of all receptors which enter into the analyzer is reflected. Of course, the number of symbols in this "large" alphabet will be very great, almost infinite, just as the diversity of sounds or pictures is infinite.

Figure 46 offers a conditional schematic with many inputs and outputs, the receptor cells a, b, c, d being elementary transducers of the first analyzer (for example, sight). Each of these can be in state a_1, a_2, and a_3 as a function of the amount of light energy impinging on it. The combination a_1, b_2, d_1, and c_3 are equivalent to a symbol A, another combination translates into symbol B, and so forth. The "large" alphabet is very great. The same procedure applies to the second analyzer with its particular large and small alphabets. And there is still another, an even higher-level alphabet—combination of "large" letters of each analyzer, for example, α = B, N.

The hierarchical alphabets reflect the static situation. However, in reality, everything changes; having divided time into portions (quanta) and having recorded the state during each of these according to various letters of an alphabet (at any level), we obtain a word which reflects the change of the external world with time. Collections of words comprise a dictionary. If we take small intervals of time, then many sequentially proceeding words will be necessary for the description of a prolonged process. For economy of memory it is advantageous to use hierarchical dictionaries. Moreover, the specific sequence of words which represent, as it were, a phrase is replaced by a new symbol—by a word from the dictionary at a higher level. Each such "higher"-level word designates the meaning of a chain of events. Letters, alphabets, words, dictionaries—these are hierarchical information codes.

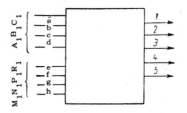

FIG. 46. Schematic of a conditional system with many inputs and outputs.

Let us turn to the outputs. They are shown to the right of the square which designates the system. Each number corresponds to a single muscle. The various degrees of contraction of this muscle are represented by the letters of the particular output alphabet, for example, 1a, 1b, 1c. Combination of letters of individual analyzers can be designated by the roman numerals: I, II, III, IV, and so forth. Each such letter corresponds to a pose. A collection of poses in time designates a word which corresponds to movement. Complexes of movements can be designated by words taken from a higher hierarchical dictionary in which the words correspond to entire motor acts—and thus one may step up to complex labor operations.

In essence the information processing consists of the following:

1. Transducers-receptors sense the external world and code it in the form of letters, at first, of the simplest lower alphabets. A change of state of the transducer with time is remembered in temporary memory in the form of some simple word.

2. Then a program of recognition proceeds with hierarchical recoding of the information. According to the collection of small letters (a, b, c), an image is distinguished—A, B, M, N, and so forth. Recognition of the words proceeds at the same time, also going from a lower to a higher level. Each level has temporary memory in which words are stored for some time (this is necessary for recognition for the time being).

Recognition itself represents a sequential comparison of words taken from temporary memory with standards of words taken from permanent memory. On all levels comparison proceeds according to a probabilistic basis, not requiring exact identity. For this to take place the word is taken from temporary memory and converted into a form suitable for comparison with the standards.

The hierarchical principle of recoding of information described above makes it possible to decrease the volume of memory but realization of the automaton does not depend on the use of this technique. Machines can remember great outputs of information recorded in a lower-level code, this in the form of a long collection of words comprised of "small" letters $(a, b, \ldots, e)$, and if it possesses a large memory and "rapid action," it can compare these with a collection of long phrases from permanent memory recorded in the very same "language." For example, a man observes the external world and simultaneously recognizes it according to its elements, integrates these in his brain and comprehends the meaning. In motion pictures he sees battle scenes and directly compares each new film with old ones which were already designated by the symbol "war." Of course, such a principle of recognition of images and events are suitable only for relatively simple pictures (for words). For complex ones, hierarchical recoding is essential.

There are many different ways to implement such hierarchical recoding, the choice among these being dependent on the available technology. Various programs which permit electronic computers to discriminate sound and sight images have been developed in many laboratories. Language constitutes the basis of such programs, that is, the collection of letters in alphabets and the collections of words composed of these letters. All this is stored in permanent memory along with the program of comparison. Of course, images and events of the external world are recognized only if there already exist standards for them in the dictionary.

It is possible to reflect the level of energy of models and the penetrability of connections between them in a program of hierarchical information processing. In the absence of an amplifying system, the energy of a model in temporary memory can be registered by a supplementary coefficient with each letter of the alphabet or word. This energy is sensed from the external environment, being dependent on the intensity of the stimulus. After comparison of the model in temporary memory with the standards taken from permanent memory one is selected for transmittal to a higher level, the coefficient of energy will change at the same time, but this in a reduced form.

With each model of a letter or word there is a record of its address and the penetrability of the various connections. All this is considered in the process of comparing the words of temporary with those from the permanent memory. Moreover, for each word in temporary memory, that word is selected from the permanent memory which has a corresponding letter at a higher level. Each between level connection has a specific penetrability—a resistance, so that crossing from level to level requires an expenditure of energy. If the energy of a word is too small, then the word recorded in a lower code will not be recognized, that is, neither letters nor a short word in a higher level will be located for it.

A program for the formation of associations, that is, for making new connections, can also be reproduced on an electronic computer. In one variant, where information arrives simultaneously along two channels (from two analyzers), still another temporary memory is introduced in which combinations of letters or words received from both channels are stored. If, two words coincide an expected number of times during some prechosen segment of time, then still another address and coefficient of penetrability will be entered in the model-standard from each word. Consequently, when this word subsequently obtains a specific level of energy, as a result of comparison with a word from temporary memory, then excitation from it can pass to a word in another block of memory which corresponds to another analyzer. In the final analysis, all words in the permanent memory of an analyzer "will overgrow" with new connections, each having its own coefficient, this leading into different blocks of memory. The path for the further distribution of excitation from the first model is determined by the comparison of the resistance of the connections—the excitation being directed along the more penetrable of these. Thus the flow of thoughts is reproduced as the sensed information is processed (recognition).

It is possible to model the formation of a new level in the very same way. For this it is necessary to remember the order of the words in the already existing level, and if these are systematically repeated (the phrase is repeated), then a new word in a higher level is established for it. It is particularly important that this new word or letters simultaneously develop associations with other dictionaries.

According to the same principle, it is possible to create blocks of models of mixed concepts—so-called supplementary codes. They represent a higher model (a letter or word), uniting words (or letters) from the alphabets of different analyzers. For these, a new block of memory is formed which might be called the "block of mixed concepts." Its words have associative connections with other blocks, these being established in the process of activity.

Models of this kind already represent the realization of a structural method of modeling.

Motor programs are modeled according to a structural schematic only. Since movement always develops in time, every similar program can be represented by a collection of hierarchical words. Moreover, each letter of a word at a higher level corresponds to an entire word on a lower level. In turn, letters of this lower level are realized by entire words on a still lower level. The whole program represents a hierarchical recoding from "top to bottom."

Let us dwell on the role of energy and of connections. A "letter for the energy" is placed next to each word—this being a coefficient of the model. Connections are represented by addresses of the underlying models which are "secured" to each letter of the word. Here then is a coding for the coefficients of resistance of the connections.

Programs can be rigid or flexible. The former are characterized by unambiguous correspondence of hierarchical words, in the latter, however, for each letter of a higher word only one of several words on a lower level is to be activated. The selection of this word is realized according to the following criteria: a) the most well-worn connections; b) the greatest "preparedness," that is, the highest level of specific energy; signals concerning this move through feedback connections; and c) the corresponding elements of a word must not be occupied in other programs. Because of these criteria a single concrete program is formed from among the many possible ones. Besides, lower levels are selected not only according to the connection and signals from "below," but also according to the combined influence of other higher models (codes-qualities), which, in sending energy to them, raise the degree of readiness.

As already mentioned above, a good motor program must be ensured with feedback signals from executive organs or, more accurately, from models-words of the underlying levels. Just as essential is the signaling received from the object of the influence. Consequently, in a complex of motor programs it is essential to include auxiliary information processing programs which operate according to general principles, but closely associated with the basic program which serves it.

Besides feedback connections, which sense and carry signals, it is also necessary to have servosystems wherein a model of the required feedback information is reflected and the degree of coincidence with respect to the "actual" information obtained from the periphery—from lower levels and from the object of influence, can be verified. In practice, this is a word activated simultaneously with the motor program; another word is compared with it, this one being obtained from "below" in the process of execution of the program and the reception of information from the working organs and from the external environment. The level of energy and "tempo" —the factor of time, enters these words in the form of coefficients. A signal which activates supplementary programs of amplification or inhibition of the main one is called upon if there is disagreement between the "required" and the "actual" information concerning execution of the motor program.

Realization of a similar program on an electronic computer is completely possible. It would involve a structural schematic with variants at lower levels along with feedbacks and servosystems. The program would be comprised of alternate "checking" of all chains which are associated with one another. In essence, this checking reduces to a determination of the changes in the level of energy of each of the elements (the model, the letter) in time. With respect to the external characteristics of activity of a system only changes of energy of the working elements which replace muscles are of interest.

The necessity to introduce such important complications as variants at lower levels, feedbacks, servosystems, and supplementary correcting subprograms, is dictated by the desire to obtain an optimum program of activities, computed to be adaptive to the "object of influence," that is, to its resistance. If the automaton were concerned with an object which could not change, then the whole program could be made simple and rigid.

It is possible to further complicate and improve the program of activities by introducing an element of self-improvement by way of remembering the effectiveness of each executed program and the subsequent selection of the most successful variant. It is even possible to assign a special program of search for the best variant with respect to a "premediated" change of the program. To accomplish this one must have criteria for the effectiveness which pertain to the precision and speed of execution of the motor act and the loss of energy or reduction of the number of participating "muscles."

To start such a program, it is essential to remember the different variants of execution of the program and their individual effectiveness so as to subsequently compare and select the optimum one—to change the order and composition of the letters in the words and the coefficients of the connections between them. Of course, it is quite difficult for electronic computers to realize this complication in view of the required volume of memory, the complexity of composition, and the time of execution of the programs. The whole point is that in the nervous system all these functions are executed by identical nerve cells but in electronic computers every function has a corresponding type of element.

The problem of modeling the process of the creation of complex programs, as this occurs in a child in the course of training, is another matter. In principle, this problem is completely solvable although it is most complex. Let me state the problem only in brief. For the creation of a program it is necessary to be concerned with certain elements—with those random motor reactions which are inherent to the child, and criteria for the evaluation of the corresponding effect. In other words: it is necessary to set up a program of trials, guide ourselves by certain criteria for the evaluation of their effectiveness and select those which are most nearly ideal. Formation then proceeds from "below to above": at first simple programs of elementary motor acts are created and then to the degree required higher levels are created on this basis—words of complex programs. In essence, it is necessary to establish connections between the hierarchical models of the sensed information and the corresponding models of activities. Evidently, the program of imitation is a very important element of this process of direct computation using muscle activities derived from sight or sound images. This relates to the copying not only of simple movements but of higher-level movements as well.

Modeling of the feeling sphere presents no particular difficulty. Feelings in an automaton is a program of parallel information processing which reflects its independence. It reacts to external influences not "in general," but in such a way as to obtain the greatest benefit from certain of its own programs—those represented in the organism by the instincts "for one's self," and "for the family." Consequently, first of all, it is necessary to construct a model of these innate programs which must be submitted to an evaluation of the effectiveness of the resulting behavior.

Simple feelings, originating from the subcortex, can be presented in the form of stable models in which the needs of the body for food, for defense from harmful external influences, and for reproduction are reflected. Programs of activities in the subcortex are represented by elementary "desires"—by simple reactions of the type "to seize," "to run away," and others. Particular feelings (hunger, thirst, cold) have connections with universal feelings of "pleasure" and "displeasure," which are the basic criteria for the evaluation of the external environment and one's own activities.

Programs of emotions are special programs of amplification which are activated under specific exceptional circumstance. Their schematic was shown above. Modeling it, evidently, is not complex. The centers of emotions have many connections with other sections of the subcortex.

Internal stimuli, that is, the excitation of centers of the subcortex, have direct reflection in the cortex according to certain general rules. It is also possible to model these in the form of letters in their own alphabet, in general, this being simpler than in external ones. Their change with time is reflected in words. The laws of hierarchical information processing also relate to cortical models of feelings. From the latter, higher hierarchical alphabets are generated—complex feelings which represent combinations of several simple ones. It is possible to imprint prolonged changes of feelings in time in the form of words. The intensity of feelings is reflected in the form of energy—here by a supplementary letter or by a coefficient in words. It all depends on the influence from within the body.

The relation of feelings to the external stimuli is reflected in the form of associative connections between the various models, each having different penetrability. A model of each external stimulus (a letter) can activate a feeling and can itself be activated from the internal sphere, from the feelings. Since a model of a conditioned stimulus has connections with several (sometimes opposite) feelings, the selection between them takes place according to the same principles as does the selection of motor subprograms: according to the degree to which the connections have been well-worn, according to the preparedness of the model of feelings, this being a consequence of its excitation from "below"—from the body.

Centers of feelings from the subcortex are not independent, they are subordinate only to the internal sphere. Excitation "descends" to them from the cortex, from conditioned stimuli, raises or lowers their activity and in this way takes part in the regulation of internal organs. It is essential to provide for this in the model.

In general, it is necessary to realize modeling of the feeling sphere and of its connections with logical programs according to the "structural" principle, assigning models of feelings to the cortex and the subcortex, forming associative connections, and establishing the level of energy of the models.

It is necessary to investigate the participation of feelings according to this same principle in perception, in information processing, and in the programs of one's own activities.

Thus, for example, the subjectivity of perception is expressed as a comparison with models from temporary memory, those models-standards are first "served" which possess stable connections and are also the most prepared, that is, which have the greatest activity and consequently require minimal transmission of energy. This preparedness is created because of the arrival of energy from areas related to the models of feelings, especially if these are stable connections and the feelings themselves are strongly "charged" by excitation from the body. Since comparison is realized according to the probabilistic principle, the amplification of some models in permanent memory and weakening of others can lead to the selection of "similar ones," and not only those which are the most accurate in terms of coincidence. It is also possible to model this if the probabilistic principle of comparison is realized, but this sharply complicates the program.

The feeling element in the selection of a program of activities and its realization plays a still larger role. A schematic for such a program was shown in Fig. 23. Here the problem of modeling consists of reproducing the transmission of excitation from the model of the stimulus sensed from the external world on any level to a model on a higher level of the program of activity—to its "idea." Connections suitable for this exist in many completely different subprograms. It is therefore necessary to select one of them, and as a general rule, that one is selected which has the most stable connections and the most excited model (the greatest preparedness). The external stimulus excites feelings according to their associations, these in turn excite models "of elementary desires," and the latter raise the energy (the excitability) of the models of the activities. This is the simplest variant. It is possible to complicate this program, proceeding from a general plan of activities. This embraces the activation of servosystems and foresight of the results. There are three such systems and one of them is the feeling system. In it are reflected the feelings imprinted in memory which develop in the course of execution of sequential activities. It should be noted that models of feelings are associated with the subcortex which alters their energy (their excitability). Therefore, foresight of feelings is a process which reflects not only features taken from memory but also the feeling "situation" which exists at the given time. As a result of executing the program of foresight of feelings it may turn out that initial "excitation" will be blocked by the expectation of unpleasantness at the end of the activities. As already indicated, the comparison of "particular" feelings is realized according to their connections with the universal feeling of "pleasure" or of "displeasure."

In the process of executing a program, various feelings may develop as a result of "disagreement" of a model of foresight in the servosystem with actual reality. These feelings must be stored in a special temporary memory so as to subsequently change the model stored in the feeling servosystem. Of course, modeling of this process, again requires supplementary memory, time, and the labor of programmers.

The formation of new programs of activity is realized with the necessary participation of feelings. In response to an unknown stimulus, elementary programs of search are instituted and trial activities are activated, the result being registered not only as to the effectiveness of the influence on the external cause, but mainly in terms of the feelings of "pleasure" or "displeasure" which accompany the search. These are remembered and upon repetition of the activity of the stimulus, promote or inhibit activation of the corresponding approved program. It is possible to model this process with a variety of complications.

As noted above, besides the feelings which are associated with the internal sphere and their derivatives, there exist still other sources of feelings—complex reflexes, which yield sensations approaching bodily feelings and eliciting excitations, desires.

In an informational way, complex reflexes can be conceived to exist in the form of supplementary programs of information processing, sensations—as supplementary codes-quantities, and excitations—as certain elementary programs of activities which can be superimposed on basic logical programs. We will briefly discuss the possibility of modeling these.

1. The orientation reflex "What is it?" The whole program of hierarchical information processing reduces itself to a recognition-search of models-standards for comparison with the models in temporary memory. It is possible to assume the existence of a special servosystem, which "supervises" this process. An unidentified model which remains in temporary memory is registered by the servosystem as a disagreement and this activates a special

model of the sensation of curiosity. Energy radiates from it, thus increasing the potential (the degree of excitation) of this model in temporary memory and this promotes the continuation of search— this by the piercing of poorly paved connections. The amount of this energy depends on the degree of excitation of the model of the sensation of curiosity, this being amplified with conditioning and possibly also dependent on age and experience.

2. The reflex of imitation. As already noted its essence lies in the automatic computation of information derived from sight and sound models. In all probability, this is an innate quality inherent to many animals. It can be conceived and modeled as a special program comprised of a model of feeling or of desire to imitate, and the computation itself as a direct transmission of excitation from certain simple models to the motor sphere. Usually, this concerns comparatively simple motor acts, but it may affect complex hierarchical models as well, for example, the concept of "mode."

3. The reflex of goal is the need to complete an activity once begun, this being a kind of inertia. It is possible that this is an adaptation to a servosystem in the form of a higher level, in which both the beginning and end of the program is reflected. This model is activated together with the excitation of a program of activities, is always in a state of increased activity and is disengaged only when a signal arrives concerning the execution of the program. If the activity is slowed by virtue of an excessive resistance of the object, that is, because of the insufficiency of energy in the program, then the signal concerning this enters the model of the reflex of goal; an impulse is then directed from this model, thus amplifying the program.

4. The reflex of freedom is a certain feeling which arises in the presence of noise which interferes with the realization of any function and activates the desire to destroy these noises. Its model is represented in the form of a servosystem, similar to (or even the same as) the model of the previous reflex, which registered difficulties in the operations and which activate the system for the discrimination of cause and a program of activities aimed at the destruction of these difficulties. This problem is best solved with participation of the amplifying system of attention.

5. Modeling of time can be represented in the form of a "delay" in the transmission of excitation from one model to another. However, there are sensations associated with time, for example, expectation, impatience. It is possible to represent these as models associated with "clocks."

Thus, the entire program of sensing, data processing, and the delivery of information is realized with continual participation of the feeling sphere which is, so to speak, the watchman of the interests of the individual in complex situations. For an automaton, this is a servosystem which continually verifies the optimality of its behavior according to certain criteria stored within it. These criteria can in themselves be altered according to a specific assigned program (as with age in man) or it can depend on exercise, on memory, that is, it can participate in the processes of self-organization, this also according to a specific law.

The modeling of speech can be reduced to the creation of parallel programs for the processing of sensed information and of other specific activities.

As already indicated, speech promotes the formation of complex concepts, since the word emerges as that conditioned signal with which higher levels of information processing in concrete images are associated. Most probably this process can be reconstructed in terms of a type of neuron network.

The parallel activity of two programs is also necessary in such modeling. For this, one could make use of the usual models and join them in programs for speech in which concrete images are replaced by words, this in relation to both sensed information and motor programs. All information is expressed by the verbal code, while the words have associative connections with feelings and with concrete images. Switching-over from one program to another occurs according to the general laws of association as a function of the resistance of the connections and of the potential energy.

Programs of consciousness and subconsciousness are of the greatest interest since it is these that distinguish man from animals and account for the specificity of information processing by the brain as a modeling apparatus.

As already noted, in the concepts of inputs and outputs—of alphabets and words, the intensity of the stimulus or of the activity is a factor. It is possible to represent this intensity as a separate letter which is added to the basic letters of the alphabet. This index essentially depends on supplementary inputs—on feelings. The external world is highly varied. In the complex of a large letter of the alphabet (A, B, ...) or of a word of few letters, a small letter can be included as a component which characterized the "energy." According to this idea, each large letter must have a corresponding word at the output. However, the large alphabet is so great that there is no possibility to locate a separate word for each letter. In other words: One cannot find an individual's particular behavior for each combination of the numerous external stimuli. This is impossible because of the significant volume of information analyzed. Therefore the organism is compelled to react not to the whole (usually unrepeated) situation, but to its separate components, the diversity of which is far less and for which there are standards and programs of activities in the memory. Thus, in one general picture there may be several such complexes, each of these having its own program, its own word at the output (in Fig. 47 models 1, 2, 3). Moreover, this advantageous activity frequently beccmes impossible, since the particular activities elicited by the separate complexes of a situation interfere with one another. Hence, there is a direct necessity to isolate and to amplify one of the complexes and suppress all of the others. With this, activity may not be optimal, but at least it becomes feasible. Such selection of one complex at the input, and the ensuring of the execution of the program of activities appropriate to it (words at the output) must be provided for by the internal program of information processing which establishes the correspondence of outputs to inputs. It is just this problem that is resolved by the first degree of consciousness—by attention. Its essence consists in the isolation of one word at the input from a number of many others which act simultaneously and of its amplification at the expense of internal energy. After this there follows a selection of a corresponding word at the output and also its amplification so as to suppress the activation of other outputs which correspond to other simultaneously operating stimuli (to words at the input). This selection occurs according to the principle of comparison of the "energetics" letter in individual words γ of the input which characterizes the intensity of the external stimulus. The second component for comparison is the force of feeling which enters into the composition of the word. In this, the "interest" of the automaton is reflected as an integrated independent system. Amplification can be connected to any partial input or output and then switched over to others (see Chapter IV).

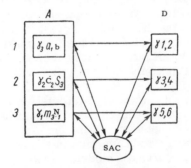

FIG. 47. Situation at the input is represented by the letter A and consists of separate complexes 1, 2, 3. For each such combination there is its own particular output— program D. Activation of one of these is determined by the connecting up of "attention" from SAC—to that one in which the component letter of energy will be the greatest.

It is characteristic that information arriving along many inputs (see Figs. 2, 3) at the same time as the first (amplified) input, continues to be processed, that is, words are composed from the letters, they are recognized, and so forth, but all of this occurs within the limits imposed by the low energetic component (Y). This is subconsciousness. The volume of information processed in it is very great, greater than in the consciousness.

The system of amplification is very closely associated with feelings—it is nourished from them by energy.

The amplifying and inhibiting system (the SAC) in fact controls all the "energetics" of the brain and it determines direction of information processing. However, it itself is only an instrument of the cortical models which are the product of external influences and the integration of the processes of self-organization.

Practical questions of the modeling of consciousness and subconsciousness may be reduced to the following:

1. All cortical models from permanent memory necessarily have two-way connections with the amplifying and inhibiting system (the SAC). The resistance of the connections can be small, and possibly variable, but for the time being I find it difficult to suggest the character of these.

2. The hypothetical structure of the SAC itself (shown in Fig. 32) consists of sensing and transmitting mechanisms. The sensors obtain data concerning the level of activity (the potential) of all models through equal (and possibly, even different) intervals of time and thus there is a selection of the most active model. The transmitting mechanism sends amplifying impulses to this model, which change its potential according to a certain curve so that at the end of the period the activity drops sharply and, at the moment of the next comparison the amplifying activity is reduced to zero (although not expiring without a trace). Simultaneously inhibiting potentials, are sent to all other models, these in the form of "negative" energy—but this only temporarily within the limits of a cycle.

3. The SAC has its own characteristics—the length of the cycle, the curve of amplification with maximum and minimum levels, a dependence between inhibition and amplification. All these parameters occur as a function of the influences on the SAC from without—from cortical models, from models of feelings from the subcortex, and from the endocrine system. It is necessary to concern ourselves with these dependencies.

4. It is essential to have "energetic" characteristics for cortical models of the type shown in Figs. 43 and 44, for nerve networks. As yet it is unclear what the interaction is between the impulses (the energy), obtained by the model from other models and from the SAC. If the former can raise the activity of certain cells for a long time, mainly at a higher level, then the latter must yield only transitory, though high amplification, which leaves only insignificant aftereffects. It is very important to concern ourselves with the dynamic characteristics of conditioning of cortical models—with the increase of their particular activity (or of their excitability) after repeated participation in "conscious" acts.

The "principle of self-amplification" is based on this and explains many purely human peculiarities of the mind—social programs, fascination, and others.

Modeling of the processes of information processing on the level of consciousness leads to calculation of the sequence and speed of movement of excitation from one cortical model to another. This determines the direction of the flow of thought or of the selection of higher codes from the sensed information, for the determination of supplementary codes-qualities, or for the activation of motor programs with all their arsenal of servosystems. The movement of the basic flow of energy is computed according to associations. In essence, this is the model of thought.

It is much more difficult to imagine and even more difficult to model information processing in the subconscious. For this it is necessary to compute the circulation of energy between all of the models located in memory. We cannot manage without this since the material for consciousness is prepared in the subconscious— the level of energy of models is altered, that level which must be represented in the SAC for the sake of comparison so as to select the model subject to amplification.

All of the above testifies first of all to the huge scale of computing operations which must precede the modeling of only the first step of consciousness—of attention. In fact this can be reduced to calculation of nerve networks. Of course, certain possible assumptions would facilitate this work. For example, it is possible to disregard in the calculation models which have a particular energy level lower than a specific value. In reality this is the way it goes: our thoughts revolve around a comparatively small number of objects, and all others are stored in memory unused until that time when they will be required by the influence of certain external or internal stimuli. All characteristics can be given in a crude discrete form and this facilitates the computing operation. Unfortunately, both simplifications can be harmful in the modeling of certain complex and prolonged processes.

In any case, without models of consciousness and subconsciousness as the most important instrument of the cortex, it is impossible to model complex mental functions.

As already indicated, the second step of consciousness is to model the characteristic "I" of a complex of programs of social behavior, of models of time, of will, of creativity, and of labor. General algorithms of these programs were presented above. It is possible to model them according to the principles of structural modeling.

"I" is a model which has a mass of connections with models of feelings, of activities, as a result of which complex models are obtained: such as "I feel," "I do." In contrast to this, other models are created—for the second and for the third persons. Their formation is impossible without words, although in themselves they represent derivative concrete images, and not their verbal equivalents. Of course, these concepts can be modeled on the basis of words and then transferred to concrete images; the creation of mixed models is also possible: "I"—this is a word, but "I do" is a model at a higher level than the concrete muscle contractions taken from servosystems.

Models of third persons are constructed by the very same principles: at first the form of man (a concrete image) is associated with a concrete name, then with the abstract "He." Activities of the third person are sensed according to a visual image, they are designated by the very same word that designates one's own activities since they have the very same form; such as "he is writing." In all probability, formation of these images begins inversely—first from the third person, since the child is initially trained to see others, and only later, himself. It is just because of this that he calls himself for a long time not "I," but rather by his name: "Kolya cries."

Formation of verbal models which designate person and activity, creates the first condition for the transfer of the sensations of others to oneself—thus man learns to understand others. Certainly it is possible to model this according to a structural scheme in which parallel models of words and of images are represented.

Formation of the concept of time presents great difficulties and all the more so in the modeling of it. Usually time is associated with activity—this finds expression even in language in the form of different times. Algorithms for the concepts of present, future, and past were explained in a previous chapter. The present time is comprised images from temporary memory, the past—from permanent memory and future is formed according to a complex program of foresight inherent in its simplest form to each program of activity. An appeal to past time is recollection, to the future—imagination. These are realized according to a direct assignment, or proceeding from established programs of investigation of the object, or, finally, accidentally.

For the modeling of recollection it is first necessary to create models of the sequence of memorization of events in connection with a calculation of time. I assume that this is entirely possible. Part of the clearest pictures (possessing the greatest potential) will be memorized as a whole, others—in the form of economical meaning-models at higher levels (the content of events being more or less detailed). Under these conditions, recollection is that same search for a variant at a lower level as occurs in an ordinary motor program.

To turn to the past, that is, to activate a program of recollections, it is necessary that the "assignment" should come into consciousness in the form of the word "recall" or different questions about the past which contain the same "upper" word, according to which it it necessary to reestablish words or letters from a lower alphabet.

Modeling of this process is realized according to the general rules of models of the "flow of thought"—with the switching-over of attention-amplification from one model to another, and among these to the past.

Modeling of a program of imagination is perhaps more complex. Turning to the future is activated just as recollection is—by direct order, by a generalized program of investigation or, finally, if attention is accidentally switched-over to a word—by command. A program of foresight of the future reduces to the following: In memory there are hierarchical words for different events: on a lower level—this is the order of succession of pictures, at higher levels—their meaning, in supplementary levels—their different qualities. When one must estimate the future of an already known system, it is only necessary to activate a chain of events—to find a letter in a word which corresponds to the state of the system at the given time, then all foresight becomes recollection, that is, a restoration of the order of change of a system—of the sequence of letters in a word beginning from the given one. In the absence of the precise model of the events in memory an "assembly" is possible of lower levels according to the various codes-qualities of the upper levels which are mentioned in the assignment. Moreover, different "pieces" of a model can be taken from the most diverse regions of memory so long as they come near to the assigned upper codes-qualities. Such is the mechanism of fantasy.

The model "I" has connections with many other models. These reflect the relation of the object represented by them to the subject, to his feelings. Therefore, the feeling program of information processing has direct relation to the model "I" or, more accurately, in it the "I" is personified. However, this does not mean, that feelings, embodied in this model, reflect only "animal" programs of instincts. Man does not belong to himself alone—he is a member of society. Programs "for species-society" are particularly powerful in him and they are also transformed into feelings.

Still another program of parallel information processing which is a characteristic quality of human consciousness is the evaluation of information from the point of view of social morality and ethics. In the process of upbringing, rules of social behavior are inculcated in man, as are such concepts as "duty," "honor," "conscience," and "shame." These represent higher codes-qualities which are formulated with the necessary participation of speech, from sensed and imparted information. All these models comprise their own type of matrix upon which is superimposed all newly arriving information for its evaluation. The principle of operation is exactly like that for the primitive feeling program: remembering of the sensed picture in temporary memory, the generation from it of higher codes, comparison of their models with models-standards which in a given case are expressed by concepts of social behavior. As a result of comparison, models are distinguished and these activate the appropriate feelings which have been inculcated by upbringing—this being accomplished by the type of conditioned reflexes of stable associative connections developed with the centers of "pleasure" and of "displeasure." Feelings activate desires and by this exert influence on the selection of a program of the individual's behavior.

The algorithm of this program is understandable, but modeling it will be difficult mainly because it is necessary to select very high codes of information.

Human behavior obeys the general law: external influences are sensed and are modeled with the generation of different levels, and from these models programs of activities are activated. To hierarchical words at the output correspond hierarchical words at the input. Man is distinguished from animals in that these words are long, sometimes embracing segments of time which can be measured in decades. The formation of output programs in him is very complex: it occurs with the participation of logical, feeling, and social programs of information processing, with elements of will and of creativity.

I will not dwell on modeling of complex programs of willful activities, of creativity, and of labor. Their algorithms were briefly described above. In principle, it is possible to create models according to them, but it is difficult to say whether we will be able to realize this on contemporary machines in view of the very great volume of computation required. One cannot imagine them in primitive form. It is necessary to create consciousness and subconsciousness, recollection and imagination, speech, the interaction of "animals," of social and logical programs of information processing; that is, the mind of man with all its basic elements. It seems to me that there is every reason to believe that in the not too distant future such models will be created. For this, what is most important is the principle of hierarchical information processing with the participation of several parallel subprograms.

Conclusion

Everything stated in this book is nothing more than a popular introduction to the study of modeling of the mind. To create this model, we must exert great effort in many diverse directions. I will attempt to indicate these.

First of all, theoretical investigations into general questions of information processing and in the study of systems are essential. It is necessary to make the concepts more precise and, so far as possible, familiarize those concerned with the principles of hierarchical information processing—with the concept of hierarchical codes, of hierarchical models—along with probabilistic comparison. It would be desirable to express the degree of similarity of a model to the original in a quantitative manner. At this same level there is also the question as to the quantity of selective information using hierarchical, human, and supplementary codes. All these concepts must serve as the basis for creation of artificial modeling mechanisms and as an outline for the study of natural systems of a similar type.

The physiological approach is employed to study the function of nerve cells and structures created from these cells—"programs of activity of a cell" or alternatively, their static and dynamic characteristics: the dependence of the frequency of impulses and of the duration of impulsing on different types of external influences—the inputs. It would be desirable to study these for cells of different types—as these occur in different layers and regions of the cerebral cortex and the subcortex. At the same time it is necessary to continue the investigation of the interaction of cells and of structures—to study concrete nerve networks of different complexity beginning from the sympathetic ganglion and ending with the cortex.

The creation of mathematical models of cells and structures is the goal of these physiological investigations, therefore, experiments must be conducted with exactitude and the results subjected to mathematical data processing through the use of computers. Heuristic programming, the creation of models of neurons with different characteristics and of artificial nerve networks which approach those studied in nature must be undertaken in

185

parallel with these experiments. It is very important to develop a method for the study of systems which would measure relevant characteristics: the measurement and recording of all inputs and outputs are necessary, recoding of continuous variables in terms of symbols convenient for processing by electronic computers. No matter how difficult the physiological investigation of complex nerve networks may be, they are essential since, in the final analysis, it is just these that will reveal the structure and function of the human brain, which will explain its concrete psychological and particularly its pathological properties. The problems or tasks of psychology can be reduced to a description of human behavior under different conditions. The distinction of cybernetic psychology is not the language of description. It is necessary to develop hierarchical codes for actions, for operations, for meaning, for moods, for emotions, and for other psychological concepts. The study of speech can be of great help in this regard since its system appears to model the mind well in this regard.

Experimental study of human behavior with transcriptions in terms of a relative numeric code permits one to subject the obtained results to mathematical processing and to isolate various types of people. The diversity of data which a machine is capable of processing is very great, therefore, it is possible to create a classification of types based on experiments with the continuous recording of numerous parameters. Technology permits us to relate purely psychological analysis with indices of the physiology of the lower regulating systems— the autonomic nervous system, the endocrine system.

Since man is a social being it is essential to study his social behavior. A code is necessary of the characteristic actions, for their evaluation from the point of view of existing rules and ethics.

Heuristic modeling of the mind in machines is the most important direction of this research. Although this method belongs to psychology, its independent elaboration is acceptable, and this in several ways. First of all, it is possible to model some of the general theoretical ideas of hierarchical information processes, utilizing for this any arbitrarily assigned influences and generating from the influence various hierarchical information. It is possible to model hierarchical programs of activities even with the various above-described complications. A third type of model is the interrelation of several programs both for the generation and processing of information and for activities as well. This is the most general case which occurs in the activity of the brain. A fourth type of model is the "conscious and subconscious," in other words, a program for the selection of dominating and "secondary" lines in processing of information with its profuse arrival from without and with the necessity to preserve the usefulness of particular activities.

All these models require development of structure and language. After this is done it is necessary to check and investigate their behavior with respect to hypothetical regimes of external influences and the characteristics of the individual elements and connections among these elements. Of course, modeling from the very beginning must be associated with psychology, that is, to some concrete conditions of human activity. The models may well be made more understandable and useful through adoption of the existing code of speech.

The method of heuristic modeling permits us to work either at a completely abstract level or in some degree to approach concrete hypothetical models of the brain. Unfortunately, the limitations of contemporary computers impose severe restrictions on the set of models which can be explored. They do not permit the processing of a great quantity of information, therefore, we must necessarily be limited either to the modeling of psychological functions with respect to only significant information, or to create "the entire man" but this with a sharp reduction in the sphere of his activity.

One can imagine an infinite number of combinations of different programs of the human mind, each, adapting to the aims of a specific investigation or to concrete problems of technology.

Because it is the principle of activity of computers which limits the possibilities for modeling, the scientists and engineers must immediately face the important problem of the creation of mechanisms which imitate complex nerve networks and the associated information processing which takes place simultaneously along many channels. Specific elements and systems for their association or combination are required for this study. I will not try to make any prognosis but it seems to me that work in this direction will bring us closest to modeling of the brain.

Even the most theoretical science presumes practical utilization of its results. For the time being it is, however, possible to speak about the practical utilization of psychology only with great reservations. One must hope that the application of cybernetic theory and technology will bring this about. Education, psychology, sociology, and technology in general feel the need for it. It seems to me that it is simply unthinkable to plan the building of a new society without quantitative consideration of the psychology of its members. This important problem can be solved only through the collective effort of psychologists, physiologists, mathematicians, and engineers working together in a single institution.

Index

Acetocholine, 89
Acquired responses, distortion of, 145
Adrenal system, activity of, 120
Adrenalin, 89
  effect of, 62
  secretion of, 92
Amino acids, chains of, 14
Analog computers (see Computers)
Anatomical cortex, 52
Antagonism, defined, 17
Aorta, backpressure in, 149
Arresting device, 162
Associations, formation of, 171
Attention-amplification, 116
  program of, 117
Attention mechanism, 115
Automaton, memoryless, 154
  with memory, 154
Autonomic centers, higher, 120
Axons, 60

Bikov's cortical hypothesis, 31
Black box method, 167
Brain, biochemistry of, 144
  function of, 186
  pathological properties of, 186
  psychological properties of, 186
  structure of, 51, 186
Brain stem, reticular formation of, 86

Cardiovascular system, 30
Causality, principle of, 13
Cells, cortical, functional hypertrophy of,
  144
  embryonic, DNA of, 167
  epithelial, 60
  excitation of complex of, 127
  maturity of, 41
  molecular structure of, 155
  nerve, cortical, hierarchical structure of,
  147

Cells (cont'd.)
  principle of biology of, 72
  pyrimidal, extensions of, 51
  sex, alteration of DNA in, 35
Cellular levels, 59
  study of, 60
Cerebral cortex, generation of information
  in, 9
  programs of, 67
  schematic of, 67
Channels, mainline, 52
  secondary, 52
Chekov, A., 128
Chemical secretion, 43
Chemical transformations, principles of, 39
Chemistry of joy, 91
Cognition, defined, 23
  as modeling, 23
Cognition-modeling, process of, 23
Complex codes, formation of, 79, 96
Complex feelings, origin of, 97
Complex organisms, study of cellular pro-
  grams of, 60
Complex systems, modeling of, 148
  programs of, 3
    basic, 36
Component, feeling, 66
  motor, 66
Computation, program of, 53
Computers, analog, 155, 162
  digital, 154
Concept of loss, 91
Conditioned reflexes, 44, 45
Connections, conductivity of, 130
Consciousness, concept of, 113
  level of, 118
  programs of, 114
  threshold of, 135
Contractile fibrils, distribution of, 101
Contraposition, principle of, 90
Control organ, concept of, 98
Cortex, mute zones of, 144
  surface area of, 51

189